Course   KINA 2378
Lab Manual for
Applied Fitness Concepts
LAMAR UNIVERSITY

http://create.mheducation.com

ISBN-10: 1308684312   ISBN-13: 9781308684314

Contents

Credits

Physical Activity: Special Considerations 75

Nutrition and Body Composition 93

Lab Activities

All end-of-concept Lab Activities are available in *Connect* and can be edited, assigned, completed, submitted, and graded online. Students simply upload completed labs to their instructor.

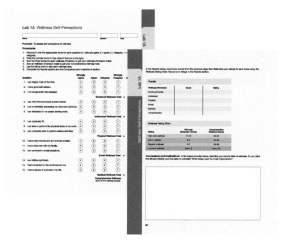

Highlights of the Seventeenth Edition

The seventeenth edition of *Concepts of Physical Fitness* is designed to deliver an integrated print and digital program that continues to be at the cutting edge of physical activity and health promotion, empowering students to take positive steps toward developing a lifelong commitment to healthy and active living. With its hallmark modular approach called "concepts," the new edition has been thoroughly updated and offers several new features designed to enhance student learning.

Extensive revisions to the content in *Connect* add new and exciting materials for easy use by students and instructors. A variety of updated and expanded *Connect* video activities help explain complex issues and provide opportunities for personal reflection and critical thinking. New *Connect* **icons** throughout the text guide students to these and additional online assignments that help students apply the material.

Significant revisions have been made in the content to reflect new health guidelines and recommendations. A revised **physical activity pyramid** provides a unique, useful model to help students understand and apply new physical activity guidelines.

Revised concept opener pages now include **learning objectives** that guide student learning and assessment. Each concept also includes an updated **Strategies for Action** section designed to help students use the lab activities to effect personal behavior change.

Each concept also includes a variety of timely features with supplemental content. One new feature, **A Closer Look**, provides information about new and sometimes controversial information related to fitness, health, and wellness. Another, called **HP 2020**, helps students see relationships between their behaviors and broader national health goals. Other updated features in each concept include **Technology Update** (describes advances in health and fitness technology), **In the News** (highlights late-breaking fitness, health, and wellness information), and **HELP** (provides tips to show students how to *help* themselves). Follow-up questions are assignable in *Connect*, helping students develop self-management, critical thinking, and reflection skills and motivating them to apply concepts of fitness, health, and wellness in their own lives.

Key **Web Resources** at the end of each concept provide students with additional online resources that supplement the content just learned. For students who want to know more about a particular topic, a list of **Suggested Readings** is given at the end of each concept.

A detailed summary of new and updated concept-by-concept content follows:

1 **Health, Wellness, Fitness, and Healthy Lifestyles: An Introduction**
- Reorganized to highlight HELP philosophy
- New information and statistics about Healthy People 2020
- Updated statistics about health and wellness
- Revised model of health, fitness, and wellness

2 **Self-Management and Self-Planning Skills for Health Behavior Change**
- New content on social-ecological models of health and wellness

- Expanded content on SMART goals
- Specific goal-setting guidelines for people with different levels of experience
- New discussion of "Blue Zones" and characteristics of healthier environments

3 **Preparing for Physical Activity**
- Updated content on warm-up and stretching guidelines
- Revised CPR guidelines
- Clarification of the distinctions between dynamic and sport-specific warm-ups
- New discussion of "minimalist" running shoes

4 **The Health Benefits of Physical Activity**
- Revised information about hypokinetic diseases
- Updated information on links between inactivity and metabolic syndrome
- Updates on the *Exercise is Medicine* campaign

5 **How Much Physical Activity Is Enough?**
- Updated descriptions of exercise training principles
- Revised content on FITT model and applications for exercise prescription
- Updated model of the physical activity pyramid with revised guidelines
- New content on sedentary behavior and independent risks from inactivity

6 **Moderate Physical Activity: A Lifestyle Approach**
- Clarification on concept of METS and Met-Minutes
- New definitions for vigorous activity and sedentary activity
- New information on health benefits of moderate activity and metabolic fitness
- New content about the built environment and walkability

7 **Cardiovascular Fitness**
- New content on ACSM fitness guidelines (Frequency–Intensity–Time)
- Revised information on target heart rate calculations and heart rate zones
- Updated content on the benefits of vigorous exercise

8 **Vigorous Aerobics, Sports, and Recreational Activities**
- Revised presentation of aerobic exercises
- New content on patterns and trends in aerobic exercise, sport, and recreation
- New information on types (and popularity) of group exercises (e.g., Zumba®)
- Expanded content on vigorous recreation and extreme sports

9 **Muscle Fitness and Resistance Exercise**
- New information about power as a health-related fitness dimension
- New sections on functional fitness and core strength
- New depictions of isometric, isokinetic, and isotonic exercise
- Revised resistance training guidelines
- New graphics and revised content on periodization
- New discussion of the popularity of the P90X fitness program

10 **Flexibility**
- Expanded content on flexibility fundamentals and importance for health
- Clarification on factors influencing flexibility

- Importance of flexibility for functional fitness
- New content on dynamic stretching (and distinctions from ballistic stretching)
- Revised stretching guidelines

11 Body Mechanics: Posture, Questionable Exercises, and Care of the Back and Neck
- New content on causes of back pain
- Updated information on (and explanations of) microtrauma
- Strategies for correcting postural deviations
- Revised discussion on implications of poor posture
- Enhanced conceptual graphics depicting good posture and good body mechanics

12 Performance Benefits of Physical Activity
- New content on high intensity interval training (HIIT)
- New information on the importance of functional fitness for sports training
- Expanded content and models on periodization

13 Body Composition
- Revised statistics about the prevalence of obesity
- Updated information about links between obesity and health
- Revised content about basal metabolic rate and creeping obesity

14 Nutrition
- New content on MyPlate and applications for diet education
- Updated information on the dietary guidelines and strategies for implementation
- Revised content on trans fat guidelines and fat substitutes
- New content on omega 3 fatty acids, soy, and antioxidants
- New legislation on vending machines and nutritional information requirements

15 Managing Diet and Activity for Healthy Body Fatness
- New conceptual model on energy balance
- Updated information on contributions of light activity to weight control
- New content on "emotional eating" and "mindless eating"

- New model of obesogenic environments and strategies for healthy eating
- New information about public/private partnerships for obesity prevention

16 Stress and Health
- Updated figure depicting stressors and reactions to stress
- New content on discrimination experiences as a source of stress
- Updated information on individualized differences in the stress response

17 Stress Management, Relaxation, and Time Management
- Updated information about mental health benefits of physical activity
- New content and image on time use and implications for stress management
- New content on effective coping strategies
- Clarification between appraisal-focused and emotion-focused coping

18 Evaluating Fitness and Wellness Products: Becoming an Informed Consumer
- New content on nutrition quackery
- Updated information about efforts to combat fraud and quackery
- Discussion of issues with labeling of "herbal" and "natural" supplements
- New content on health literacy
- Recent rulings on exaggerated health claims on fitness shoes
- New discussion of titanium necklaces

19 Toward Optimal Health and Wellness: Planning for Healthy Lifestyle Change
- Reorganized content on factors influencing health and wellness
- Expanded content on inherited risks and using the health-care system
- New content on the impact of environmental factors (including new table)
- Guidelines for adopting healthy lifestyles

Lifestyles for Health, Wellness, and Fitness

Lab Resource Materials: The Healthy Lifestyle Questionnaire

The purpose of this questionnaire is to help you analyze your lifestyle behaviors and to help you make decisions concerning good health and wellness for the future. Information on this Healthy Lifestyle Questionnaire is of a personal nature. For this reason, this questionnaire is not designed to be submitted to your instructor. **It is for your information only.** Answer each question as honestly as possible, and use the scoring information to help assess your lifestyle.

Directions: Place an X over the "yes" circle to answer yes. If you answer "no," make no mark. Score the questionnaire using the procedures that follow.

(yes) **1.** I accumulate 30 minutes of moderate physical activity most days of the week (brisk walking, stair climbing, yard work, or home chores).

(yes) **2.** I do vigorous activity that elevates my heart rate for 20 minutes at least 3 days a week.

(yes) **3.** I do exercises for flexibility at least 3 days a week.

(yes) **4.** I do exercises for muscle fitness at least 2 days a week.

(yes) **5.** I eat three regular meals each day.

(yes) **6.** I select appropriate servings from the major food groups each day.

(yes) **7.** I restrict the amount of fat in my diet.

(yes) **8.** I consume only as many calories as I expend each day.

(yes) **9.** I am able to identify situations in daily life that cause stress.

(yes) **10.** I take time out during the day to relax and recover from daily stress.

(yes) **11.** I find time for family, friends, and things I especially enjoy doing.

(yes) **12.** I regularly perform exercises designed to relieve tension.

(yes) **13.** I do not smoke or use other tobacco products.

(yes) **14.** I do not abuse alcohol.

(yes) **15.** I do not abuse drugs (prescription or illegal).

(yes) **16.** I take over-the-counter drugs sparingly and use them only according to directions.

(yes) **17.** I abstain from sex or limit sexual activity to a safe partner.

(yes) **18.** I practice safe procedures for avoiding sexually transmitted infections (STIs).

(yes) **19.** I use seat belts and adhere to the speed limit when I drive.

(yes) **20.** I have a smoke detector in my house and check it regularly to see that it is working.

(yes) **21.** I have had training to perform CPR if called on in an emergency.

(yes) **22.** I can perform the Heimlich maneuver effectively if called on in an emergency.

(yes) **23.** I brush my teeth at least twice a day and floss at least once a day.

(yes) **24.** I get an adequate amount of sleep each night.

(yes) **25.** I do regular self-exams, have regular medical checkups, and seek medical advice when symptoms are present.

(yes) **26.** When I receive advice and/or medication from a physician, I follow the advice and take the medication as prescribed.

(yes) **27.** I read product labels and investigate their effectiveness before I buy them.

(yes) **28.** I avoid using products that have not been shown by research to be effective.

(yes) **29.** I recycle paper, glass, and aluminum.

(yes) **30.** I practice environmental protection, such as carpooling and energy conservation.

Overall Score—Total "Yes" Answers

The Healthy Lifestyle Questionnaire

Scoring: Give yourself 1 point for each "yes" answer. Add your scores for each of the lifestyle behaviors. To calculate your overall score, sum the totals for all lifestyles.

Physical Activity	Nutrition	Managing Stress	Avoiding Destructive Habits	Practicing Safe Sex	Adopting Safety Habits
1. ☐	5. ☐	9. ☐	13. ☐	17. ☐	19. ☐
2. ☐	6. ☐	10. ☐	14. ☐	18. ☐	20. ☐
3. ☐	7. ☐	11. ☐	15. ☐		
4. ☐	8. ☐	12. ☐	16. ☐		
☐ Total +	☐ Total +	☐ Total +	☐ Total +	☐ Total +	☐

Knowing First Aid	Personal Health Habits	Using Medical Advice	Being an Informed Consumer	Protecting the Environment	Sum All Totals for Overall Score
21. ☐	23. ☐	25. ☐	27. ☐	29. ☐	
22. ☐	24. ☐	26. ☐	28. ☐	30. ☐	
☐ Total +	☐ Total +	☐ Total +	☐ Total +	☐ Total =	☐

Interpreting Scores: Scores of 3 or 4 on the four-item scales indicate generally positive lifestyles. For the two-item scales, a score of 2 indicates the presence of positive lifestyles. An overall score of 26 or more is a good indicator of healthy lifestyle behaviors. It is important to consider the following special note when interpreting scores.

Special Note: Your scores on the Healthy Lifestyle Questionnaire should be interpreted with caution. There are several reasons for this. First, all lifestyle behaviors do not pose the same risks. For example, using tobacco or abusing drugs has immediate negative effects on health and wellness, whereas others, such as knowing first aid, may have only occasional use. Second, you may score well on one item in a scale but not on another. If one item indicates an unhealthy lifestyle in an area that poses a serious health risk, your lifestyle may appear to be healthier than it really is. For example, you could get a score of 3 on the destructive habits scale and be a regular smoker. For this reason, the overall score can be particularly deceiving.

Strategies for Change: In the space to the right, make some notes concerning the healthy lifestyle areas in which you could make some changes. You can refer to these notes later to see if you have made progress.

Healthy Lifestyle Ratings

Rating	Two-Item Scores	Four-Item Scores	Overall Scores
Positive lifestyles	2	3 or 4	26 to 30*
Consider changes	Less than 2	Less than 3	Less than 26

*See Special Note.

Lab 1A Wellness Self-Perceptions

Name		Section	Date

Purpose: To assess self-perceptions of wellness

Procedures

1. Place an X over the appropriate circle for each question (4 = strongly agree, 3 = agree, 2 = disagree, 1 = strongly disagree).
2. Write the number found in that circle in the box to the right.
3. Sum the three boxes for each wellness dimension to get your wellness dimension totals.
4. Sum all wellness dimension totals to get your comprehensive wellness total.
5. Use the rating chart to rate each wellness area.
6. Complete the Results section and the Conclusions and Implications section.

Question	Strongly Agree	Agree	Disagree	Strongly Disagree	Score
1. I am happy most of the time.	4	3	2	1	
2. I have good self-esteem.	4	3	2	1	
3. I do not generally feel stressed.	4	3	2	1	
			Emotional Wellness Total	=	
4. I am well informed about current events.	4	3	2	1	
5. I am comfortable expressing my views and opinions.	4	3	2	1	
6. I am interested in my career development.	4	3	2	1	
			Intellectual Wellness Total	=	
7. I am physically fit.	4	3	2	1	
8. I am able to perform the physical tasks of my work.	4	3	2	1	
9. I am physically able to perform leisure activities.	4	3	2	1	
			Physical Wellness Total	=	
10. I have many friends and am involved socially.	4	3	2	1	
11. I have close ties with my family.	4	3	2	1	
12. I am confident in social situations.	4	3	2	1	
			Social Wellness Total	=	
13. I am fulfilled spiritually.	4	3	2	1	
14. I feel connected to the world around me.	4	3	2	1	
15. I have a sense of purpose in my life.	4	3	2	1	
			Spiritual Wellness Total	=	
			Comprehensive Wellness (Sum of five wellness scores)		

In the Results below, record your scores from the previous page; then determine your ratings for each score using the Wellness Rating Chart. Record your ratings in the Results section.

Results

Wellness Dimension	Score	Rating
Emotional/mental		
Intellectual		
Physical		
Social		
Spiritual		
Comprehensive		

Wellness Rating Chart

Rating	Wellness Dimension Scores	Comprehensive Wellness Scores
High-level wellness	10–12	50–60
Good wellness	8–9	40–49
Marginal wellness	6–7	30–39
Low-level wellness	Below 6	Below 30

Conclusions and Implications: In the space provided below, describe your current state of wellness. Do you think the ratings indicate your true state of wellness? Which areas need the most improvement?

Lab Resource Materials

Use the diagram below in answering the questions in Lab 2A. It is a reproduction of Figure 2 and includes factors that influence change in healthy behaviors.

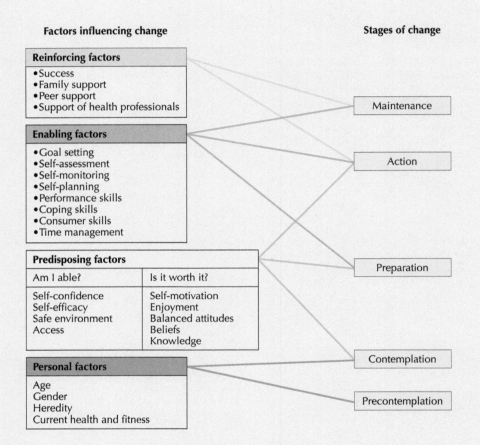

Factors influencing change

Reinforcing factors
- Success
- Family support
- Peer support
- Support of health professionals

Enabling factors
- Goal setting
- Self-assessment
- Self-monitoring
- Self-planning
- Performance skills
- Coping skills
- Consumer skills
- Time management

Predisposing factors

Am I able?	Is it worth it?
Self-confidence	Self-motivation
Self-efficacy	Enjoyment
Safe environment	Balanced attitudes
Access	Beliefs
	Knowledge

Personal factors
Age
Gender
Heredity
Current health and fitness

Stages of change

Maintenance

Action

Preparation

Contemplation

Precontemplation

Lab 2A The Stage of Change Questionnaire

Lab 2A

The Stage of Change Questionnaire

Name	**Section**	**Date**

Purpose: To help assess your current level in the stage of change hierarchy for a variety of health behaviors

Procedures

1. Determine your "readiness for change" different health behaviors using the Stage of Change Questionnaire.
2. Evaluate predisposing, enabling, and reinforcing factors for several selected behaviors.
3. Answer the questions in the Conclusions and Implications section.

Results: Complete the Stage of Change Questionnaire on the next page. List two behaviors (below) that you are interested in improving. Beside the behaviors, write your current stage for that behavior.

Behavior 1: _____   **Current Stage?**_____

Behavior 2: _____   **Current Stage?** _____

Conclusions and Implications: For each behavior, discuss the enabling, predisposing, and reinforcing factors that you think are particularly important for you as you work to change this behavior (refer to the stages of change model and Tables 1, 2, and 3 in the text).

Behavior 1:

Behavior 2:

Stage of Change Questionnaire (make one choice for each question)

1. **Physical Activity**
   ☐ Precontemplation—I am not active, and I do not plan to start.
   ☐ Contemplation—I am not active, but I am thinking about starting.
   ☐ Preparation—I am getting ready to become active.
   ☐ Action—I do some activity but need to do more.
   ☐ Maintenance—I have been active regularly for several months.

2. **Eating Well (Nutrition)**
   ☐ Precontemplation—I do not eat well and don't plan to change.
   ☐ Contemplation—I do not eat well but am thinking about change.
   ☐ Preparation—I am planning to change my diet.
   ☐ Action—I sometimes eat well but need to do more.
   ☐ Maintenance—I have eaten well regularly for several months.

3. **Managing Stress**
   ☐ Precontemplation—I do not manage stress well and plan no changes.
   ☐ Contemplation—I am thinking about making changes to manage stress.
   ☐ Preparation—I am planning to change to manage stress better.
   ☐ Action—I sometimes take steps to manage stress better but need to do more.
   ☐ Maintenance—I have used good stress-management techniques for several months.

4. **Adopting Good Safety Habits (e.g., seat belt use, safe storage of medicine)**
   ☐ Precontemplation—I have at least one unsafe habit but plan no changes.
   ☐ Contemplation—I am thinking about making changes regarding a safety habit.
   ☐ Preparation—I am planning to make a change regarding a safety habit.
   ☐ Action—I have taken action concerning a habit but need to do more.
   ☐ Maintenance—I have no safety habits that need to change (I practice good safety).

5. **Adopting Good Personal Health Habits (e.g., brushing and flossing, adequate sleep)**
   ☐ Precontemplation—I have at least one health habit that needs change but plan no changes.
   ☐ Contemplation—I am thinking about making changes related to a health habit.
   ☐ Preparation—I am planning to make a change regarding a health habit.
   ☐ Action—I have taken action concerning a habit but need to do more.
   ☐ Maintenance—I have no health habits that need to change.

6. **Learning First Aid (e.g., CPR/First Aid)**
   ☐ Precontemplation—I do not know CPR/first aid and do not plan to learn.
   ☐ Contemplation—I am thinking about learning CPR/first aid.
   ☐ Preparation—I have made plans to learn CPR/first aid.
   ☐ Action—I once knew CPR/first aid but need an update.
   ☐ Maintenance—I am up-to-date on my CPR/first aid and will keep updated.

Questions 7 and 8 are highly personal. Answer for your own use, but do not record answers on this sheet.

7. **Avoiding Destructive Habits (e.g., tobacco, drugs, alcohol)**
   ☐ Precontemplation—I have at least one destructive habit but plan no change.
   ☐ Contemplation—I am thinking about making changes related to a destructive habit.
   ☐ Preparation—I am planning to make a change regarding a destructive habit.
   ☐ Action—I have taken action concerning a habit but need to do more.
   ☐ Maintenance—I have no destructive habits or have stopped the habit for months.

8. **Practicing Safe Sex**
   ☐ Precontemplation—I have practiced unsafe sex and plan no change.
   ☐ Contemplation—I am thinking about making changes to an unsafe habit.
   ☐ Preparation—I am planning to make a change regarding an unsafe habit.
   ☐ Action—I have taken action concerning a habit but need to do more.
   ☐ Maintenance—I do not practice unsafe sex or have stopped the habit for months.

Lab 2B The Self-Management Skills Questionnaire

Name	**Section**	**Date**

Purpose: To help you assess your self-management skills that are important for three priority lifestyles (physical activity, healthy nutrition, stress management)

Procedures

1. Each question in the questionnaire on pages 41 and 42 reflects one of the self-management strategies described in this text. Each of the 12 questions requires an answer about three different healthy behaviors. Answer each question using a 3 for very true, 2 for somewhat true, or 1 for not true. Record the number of your answer in the appropriate box for each of the three healthy lifestyles.
2. After you have answered all 12 questions for each of the three lifestyles, total the three columns to get a total score for physical activity, nutrition, and stress management.
3. Determine your rating for each lifestyle using the Self-Management Skills Rating Chart. Record your rating in the Results section.
4. Answer the questions in the Conclusions and Implications section.

Results: Record your rating for each of three healthy lifestyles in the chart below.

Self-Management Skills Rating Chart

Rating	Score
Good	30–36
Marginal	24–29
Needs improvement	<24

Self-Management Skills Results	Rating
Physical activity	
Nutrition	
Stress management	

Conclusions and Implications: In several sentences, discuss your ratings regarding self-management skills related to physical activity. You may have a good total score but still have several self-management skills on which you need improvement. Comment on your overall scores and those individual self-management skills on which you had scores of 1 (not true).

The Self-Management Skills Questionnaire

In several sentences, discuss your ratings regarding self-management skills related to nutrition. You may have a good total score but still have several self-management skills on which you need improvement. Comment on your overall scores and those individual self-management skills on which you had scores of 1 (not true).

In several sentences, discuss your ratings regarding self-management skills related to stress management. You may have a good total score but still have several self-management skills on which you need improvement. Comment on your overall scores and those individual self-management skills on which you had scores of 1 (not true).

The Self-Management Skills Questionnaire	Very true	Somewhat true	Not true	Activity Score	Nutrition Score	Stress Score
1. I regularly self-assess: (self-assessment)						
personal physical fitness and physical activity levels	3	2	1	☐		
the contents of my diet	3	2	1		☐	
personal stress levels	3	2	1			☐
2. I self-monitor and keep records concerning: (self-monitoring)						
physical activity	3	2	1	☐		
diet	3	2	1		☐	
stress in my life	3	2	1			☐
3. I set realistic and attainable goals for: (goal setting)						
physical activity	3	2	1	☐		
eating behaviors	3	2	1		☐	
reducing stress in my life	3	2	1			☐
4. I have a personal written or formal plan for: (self-planning)						
regular physical activity	3	2	1	☐		
what I eat	3	2	1		☐	
managing stress in my life	3	2	1			☐
5. I possess the skills to: (performance skills)						
perform a variety of physical activities	3	2	1	☐		
analyze my diet	3	2	1		☐	
manage stress (e.g., progressive relaxation)	3	2	1			☐
6. I have positive attitudes about: (balancing attitudes)						
my ability to stick with an activity plan	3	2	1	☐		
my ability to stick to a nutrition plan	3	2	1		☐	
my ability to manage stress in my life	3	2	1			☐
7. I can overcome barriers that I encounter: (overcoming barriers)						
in my attempts to be physically active	3	2	1	☐		
in my attempts to stick to a nutrition plan	3	2	1		☐	
in my attempts to manage stress in my life	3	2	1			☐

Lab 2B

The Self-Management Skills Questionnaire

The Self-Management Skills Questionnaire

The Self-Management Skills Questionnaire	Very true	Somewhat true	Not true	Activity Score	Nutrition Score	Stress Score
8. I know how to identify misinformation: (consumer skills)						
relating to fitness and physical activity	3	2	1			
relating to nutrition	3	2	1			
relating to stress management	3	2	1			
9. I am able to get social support for my efforts to: (social support)						
be active	3	2	1			
stick to a healthy nutrition plan	3	2	1			
manage stress in my life	3	2	1			
10. When I have problems, I can get back to: (relapse prevention)						
my regular physical activity	3	2	1			
my nutrition plan	3	2	1			
my plan for managing stress	3	2	1			
11. I am able to adapt my thinking to: (coping strategies)						
stick with my activity plan	3	2	1			
stick with my nutrition plan	3	2	1			
stick with my stress-management plan	3	2	1			
12. I am able to manage my time to: (time management)						
stick with my physical activity plan	3	2	1			
shop for and prepare nutritious food	3	2	1			
perform stress-management activities	3	2	1			
Total Activity Score						
Total Nutrition Score						
Total Stress Score						

An Introduction to Physical Activity

Lab 3A Readiness for Physical Activity

Name	Section	Date

Purpose: To help you determine your physical readiness for participation in a program of regular exercise

Procedures

1. Read the directions on the "PAR-Q & You" on page 60.
2. Answer each of the seven questions on the form.
3. If you answered "yes" to one or more of the questions, follow the directions just below the PAR-Q questions regarding medical consultation.
4. If you answered "no" to all seven questions, follow the directions at the lower left-hand corner of the PAR-Q.
5. Answer the five questions about physical readiness for sports or vigorous training in Chart 1 below.
6. Record your scores below and answer the question in the Conclusions and Implications section.

Results

Chart 1 Physical Readiness for Sports or Vigorous Training

Answer the PAR-Q before using this chart. If your answer to any of these questions is "yes," you should consult with your personal physician by telephone or in person to determine if you have a potential problem with sports or vigorous training.

Yes	No	
☐	☐	**1.** Do you plan to participate on an organized team that will play intense competitive sports (e.g., varsity team, professional team)?
☐	☐	**2.** If you plan to participate in a collision sport (even on a less organized basis), such as football, boxing, rugby, or ice hockey, have you been knocked unconscious more than one time?
☐	☐	**3.** Do you currently have symptoms from a previous muscle injury?
☐	☐	**4.** Do you currently have symptoms from a previous back injury, or do you experience back pain as a result of involvement in physical activity?
☐	☐	**5.** Do you have any other symptoms during physical activity that give you reason to be concerned about your health?

Determine your PAR-Q score. Place an X over the circle that includes the number of "yes" answers that you had for the PAR-Q (see page 60).

(0)　(1)　(2)　(3)　(4)　(5)　(6)　(7)

Determine your readiness for sports or rigorous training (see Chart 1 above). Place an X over the number of "yes" answers that you had for the Physical Readiness for Sports or Vigorous Training chart.

(0)　(1)　(2)　(3)　(4)　(5)

Conclusions and Implications: In several sentences, discuss your readiness for physical activity. Base your comments on your questionnaire results and the types of physical activities you plan to perform in the future.

PAR-Q & YOU

Regular physical activity is fun and healthy, and increasingly more people are starting to become more active every day. Being more active is very safe for most people. However, some people should check with their doctor before they start becoming much more physically active.

If you are planning to become much more physically active than you are now, start by answering the seven questions in the box below. If you are between the ages of fifteen and sixty-nine, the PAR-Q will tell you if you should check with your doctor before you start. If you are over sixty-nine years of age, and you are not used to being very active, check with your doctor.

Common sense is your best guide when you answer these questions. Please read the questions carefully and answer each one honestly: check YES or NO.

YES	NO	
☐	☐	1. Has your doctor ever said that you have a heart condition <u>and</u> that you should only do physical activity recommended by a doctor?
☐	☐	2. Do you feel pain in your chest when you do physical activity?
☐	☐	3. In the past month, have you had chest pain when you were not doing physical activity?
☐	☐	4. Do you lose your balance because of dizziness or do you ever lose consciousness?
☐	☐	5. Do you have a bone or joint problem that could be made worse by a change in your physical activity?
☐	☐	6. Is your doctor currently prescribing drugs (for example, water pills) for your blood pressure or heart condition?
☐	☐	7. Do you know of <u>any other reason</u> you should not do physical activity?

If you answered

Yes

No

YES to one or more questions

Talk with your doctor by phone or in person BEFORE you start becoming much more physically active or BEFORE you have a fitness appraisal. Tell your doctor about the PAR-Q and which questions you answered YES.
- You may be able to do any activity you want—as long as you start slowly and build up gradually. Or you may need to restrict your activities to those that are safe for you. Talk with your doctor about the kinds of activities you wish to participate in and follow his or her advice.
- Find out which community programs are safe and helpful for you.

NO to all questions

If you answered NO honestly to <u>all</u> PAR-Q questions, you can be reasonably sure that you can
- Start becoming much more physically active—begin slowly and build up gradually. This is the safest and easiest way to go.
- Take part in a fitness appraisal—this is an excellent way to determine your basic fitness so that you can plan the best way for you to live actively.

DELAY BECOMING MUCH MORE ACTIVE:
- If you are not feeling well because of a temporary illness, such as a cold or a fever—wait until you feel better or
- If you are or may be pregnant—talk to your doctor before you start becoming more active.

Please note: If your health changes so that you then answer YES to any of the above questions, tell your fitness or health professional. Ask whether you should change your physical activity plan.

<u>Informed Use of the PAR-Q:</u> The Canadian Society for Exercise Physiology, Health Canada, and their agents assume no liability for persons who undertake physical activity, and if in doubt after completing this questionnaire, consult your doctor prior to physical activity.

You are encouraged to copy the PAR-Q but only if you use the entire form

*Developed by the British Columbia Ministry of Health.
Produced by the British Columbia Ministry of Health and the Department of National Health & Welfare

Physical Activity Readiness
Questionnaire • PAR-Q
(revised 2002)

Note: It is important that you answer all questions honestly. The PAR-Q is a scientifically and medically researched pre-exercise selection device. It complements exercise programs, exercise testing procedures, and the liability considerations attendant with such programs and testing procedures. PAR-Q, like any other pre-exercise screening device, will misclassify a small percentage of prospective participants, but no pre-exercise screening method can entirely avoid this problem.

Lab 3B The Stretch Warm-Up and Cool-Down

Name	Section	Date

Purpose: To familiarize you with a sample group of stretch warm-up and cool-down exercises

Procedures

1. Perform a 2- to 5-minute cardiovascular warm-up (walk, jog, slow jump rope, swim).
2. Perform the exercises in Chart 1 on page 62, including the alternative exercises, three times each. Hold the stretch for 15 to 30 seconds.
3. Complete the Results section below and answer the questions in the Conclusions and Implications section.

Results: In the following, put an X over the circle that represents the amount of tightness you felt when performing each of the stretching warm-up and cool-down exercises. Tightness indicates that you may have shortness of a specific muscle group and that stretching exercises at times other than the warm-up or cool-down are needed.

Amount of Tightness

	None	Moderate	Severe
Calf stretch	○	○	○
Hamstring stretch	○	○	○
Leg hug	○	○	○
Seated side stretch	○	○	○
Zipper	○	○	○

Alternative Exercises

	None	Moderate	Severe
Side stretch	○	○	○
Hip and thigh stretch	○	○	○
One-leg stretch	○	○	○

Conclusions and Implications: The general cardiovascular warm-up is recommended for all people. In addition, you may want to consider a stretch warm-up and stretch cool-down (as shown in this lab), or a dynamic or sport-specific warm-up option. In several sentences, discuss your experiences with the warm-up/cool-down and what you would plan to use in the future.

Chart 1 Sample warm-up and cool-down exercises

The exercises shown here can be used before a workout as a warm-up or after a workout as a cool-down. Perform these exercises slowly, preferably after completing a cardiovascular warm-up. Do not bounce. Hold each stretch for at least 15–30 seconds. Perform each exercise at least once and up to three times. Other stretching exercises are presented in the concept on flexibility, and they can be used in a warm-up or cool-down.

Cardiovascular Warm-Up
Before you perform a vigorous workout, walk or jog slowly for 2 minutes or more. After exercise, do the same. Do this portion of the warm-up prior to muscle stretching.

Calf Stretch
This exercise stretches the calf muscles (gastrocnemius and soleus). Face a wall with your feet 2 or 3 feet away. Step forward on your left foot to allow both hands to touch the wall. Keep the heel of your right foot on the ground, toe turned in slightly, knee straight, and buttocks tucked in. Lean forward by bending your front knee and arms and allowing your head to move nearer the wall. Hold. Repeat with the other leg.

Hamstring Stretch
This exercise stretches the muscles of the back of the upper leg (hamstrings) as well as those of the hip, knee, and ankle. Lie on your back. Bring the right knee to your chest and grasp the toes with the right hand. Place the left hand on the back of the right thigh. Pull the knee toward the chest, push the heel toward the ceiling, and pull the toes toward the shin. Attempt to straighten the knee. Stretch and hold. Repeat with the other leg.

Leg Hug
This exercise stretches the hip and back extensor muscles. Lie on your back. Bend one leg and grasp your thigh under the knee. Hug it to your chest. Keep the other leg straight and on the floor. Hold. Repeat with the opposite leg.

Seated Side Stretch
This exercise stretches the muscles of the trunk. Begin in a seated position with the legs crossed. Stretch the left arm over the head to the right. Bend at the waist (to right), reaching as far as possible to the left with the right arm. Hold. Do not let the trunk rotate. Repeat to the opposite side. For less stretch, the overhead arm may be bent. This exercise can be done in the standing position but is less effective.

Zipper
This exercise stretches the muscle on the back of the arm (triceps) and the lower chest muscles (pecs). Lift the right arm and reach behind the head and down the spine (as if pulling up a zipper). With the left hand, push down on the right elbow and hold. Reverse arm position and repeat.

ALTERNATE EXERCISES

Because of location (wet or hard surface), you may choose to substitute exercises that do not require you to lie down. The side stretch (standing) can be substituted for the seated side stretch, the hip and thigh stretch for the leg hug (does not stretch the same muscles), and the one-leg stretch (standing) for the hamstring stretch.

Side Stretch
This exercise stretches the trunk lateral flexors. Stand with feet shoulder-width apart. Stretch left arm overhead to right. Bend to right at waist reaching as far as possible with left arm; reach as far as possible with right arm. Hold. Do not let trunk rotate or lower back arch. Repeat on opposite side. Note: This exercise is made more effective if a weight is held down at the side in the hand opposite the side being stretched. More stretch will occur if the hip on the stretched side is dropped and most of the weight is borne by the opposite foot.

Hip and Thigh Stretch
This exercise stretches the hip (iliopsoas) and thigh muscles (quadriceps) and is useful for people with lordosis and back problems. Place right knee directly above right ankle and stretch left leg backward so knee touches floor. If necessary, place hands on floor for balance.
1. Tilt the pelvis backward by tucking in the abdomen and flattening the back.
2. Then shift the weight forward until a stretch is felt on the front of the thigh: hold. Repeat on opposite side. Caution: Do not bend front knee more than 90 degrees.

One-Leg Stretch
This exercise stretches the lower back muscles. Stand with one foot on a bench, keeping both legs straight. Contract the hamstrings and gluteals by pressing down on bench with the heel for three seconds; then relax and bend the trunk forward, toward the knee. Hold for 10–15 seconds. Return to starting position and repeat with opposite leg. As flexibility improves, the arms can be used to pull the chest toward the legs. Do not allow either knee to lock. This exercise is useful in relief of backache and correction of swayback.

Lab 3C Physical Activity Attitude Questionnaire

Name		Section	Date

Purpose: To evaluate your feelings about physical activity and to determine the specific reasons you do or do not participate in regular physical activity

Directions: The term *physical activity* in the following statements refers to all kinds of activities, including sports, formal exercises, and informal activities, such as jogging and cycling. Make an X over the circle that best represents your answer to each question.

Statement	Strongly Disagree	Disagree	Undecided	Agree	Strongly Agree	Item Score	Attitude Score
1. I should do physical activity regularly for my health.	1	2	3	4	5		Health and Fitness Score
2. Doing regular physical activity is good for my fitness and wellness.	1	2	3	4	5	+ =	
3. Regular exercise helps me look my best.	1	2	3	4	5		Appearance Score
4. I feel more physically attractive when I do regular physical activity.	1	2	3	4	5	+ =	
5. One of the main reasons I do regular physical activity is that it is fun.	1	2	3	4	5		Enjoyment Score
6. The most enjoyable part of my day is when I am exercising or doing a sport.	1	2	3	4	5	+ =	
7. Taking part in physical activity helps me relax.	1	2	3	4	5		Relaxation Score
8. Physical activity helps me get away from the pressures of daily living.	1	2	3	4	5	+ =	
9. The challenge of physical training is one reason I do physical activity.	1	2	3	4	5		Challenge Score
10. I like to see if I can master sports and activities that are new to me.	1	2	3	4	5	+ =	
11. I like to do physical activity that involves other people.	1	2	3	4	5		Social Score
12. Exercise offers me the opportunity to meet other people.	1	2	3	4	5	+ =	
13. Competition is a good way to make physical activity fun.	1	2	3	4	5		Competition Score
14. I like to see how my physical abilities compare with those of others.	1	2	3	4	5	+ =	
15. When I do regular exercise, I feel better than when I don't.	1	2	3	4	5		Feeling Good Score
16. My ability to do physical activity is something that makes me proud.	1	2	3	4	5	+ =	
17. I like to do outdoor activities.	1	2	3	4	5		Outdoor Score
18. Experiencing nature is something I look forward to when exercising.	1	2	3	4	5	+ =	

Procedures

1. Read and answer each question in the questionnaire.
2. Write the number in the circle of your answer in the box labeled "Item Score."
3. Add scores for each pair of scores and record in the "Attitude Score" box.
4. Record each attitude score and a rating for each score (use Rating Chart) in the chart below.
5. Record the number of good and excellent scores in the box provided. Use the score in the box to determine your rating using the Balance of Feelings Rating Chart.

Results: Record your results as indicated in the Procedures section.

Physical Activity Attitude Questionnaire Results

Attitude	Score	Rating
Health and fitness		
Appearance		
Enjoyment		
Relaxation		
Challenge		
Social		
Competition		
Feeling good		
Outdoor		

Attitude Rating Chart

Rating Category	Attitude Score
Excellent	9–10
Good	7–8
Fair	5–6
Poor	3–4
Very poor	2

How many good or excellent scores do you have?

Balance of Feeling Score

Balance of Feelings Rating Chart

Excellent	6–9
Good	5
Fair	4
Poor	2–3
Very poor	0–1

Having 5 or more in the box above indicates that you have a positive balance of feelings (more positive than negative attitudes).

In a few sentences, discuss your "balance of feelings" rating. Having more positive than negative scores (positive balance of feelings) increases the probability of being active. Include comments on whether you think your ratings suggest that you will be active or inactive and whether your ratings are really indicative of your feelings. Do you think that the scores on which you were rated poor or very poor might be reasons you would avoid physical activity? Explain.

Lab 4A Assessing Heart Disease Risk Factors

Name	**Section**	**Date**

Purpose: To assess your risk of developing coronary heart disease. See page 84 for directions.

Heart Disease Risk Factor Questionnaire

Risk Points

	①	②	③	④	Score
Unalterable Factors					
1. How old are you?	30 or less	31–40	41–54	55+	
2. Do you have a history of heart disease in your family?	None	Grandparent with heart disease	Parent with heart disease	More than one with heart disease	
3. What is your gender?	Female		Male		
			Total Unalterable Risk Score		
Alterable Factors					
4. Do you get regular physical activity?	4–5 days a week	3 days a week	Fewer than 3 days a week	No	
5. Do you have a high-fat diet?	No	Slightly high in fat	Above normal in fat	Eat a lot of meat and fried and fatty foods	
6. Are you under much stress?	Less than normal	Normal	Slightly above normal	Quite high	
7. Do you use tobacco?	No	Cigar or pipe	Less than 1/2 pack a day or use smokeless tobacco	More than 1/2 pack a day	
8. What is your percentage of body fat?*	F = 17–28% M = 10–20%	29–31% 21–23%	32–35% 24–30%	35+% 30+%	
9. What is the systolic number in your blood pressure?	120	121–140	141–160	160+	
10. Do you have other diseases?	No	Ulcer	Diabetes**	Both	

Extra Points: Add points for as many of the following test results as you have available: 1 point for CRP above 3, 1 point for homocysteine above 100, 3 points for LDL above 130, 3 points for TC/HDL-C above 4. If only total cholesterol is available, add 1 point for a score of 200–240 or 3 points for scores above 240.

Total Alterable Risk Score	
Extra Points	
Grand Total Risk Score	

Adapted from *CAD Risk Assessor,* William J. Stone. Reprinted by permission.

*If unknown, estimate your body fat percentage or see Lab 13A.

**Diabetes is a risk factor that is often not alterable.

Procedures

1. Complete the 10 questions and the extra points, if available, on the Heart Disease Risk Factor Questionnaire by circling the answer that is most appropriate for *you* (see front of this lab).
2. Look at the top of the column for each of your answers. In the box provided at the right of each question, write down the number of risk points for that answer.
3. Determine your unalterable risk score by adding the risk points for questions 1, 2, and 3.
4. Determine your alterable risk score by adding the risk points for questions 4 through 10.
5. Determine your total heart disease risk score by adding the scores obtained in steps 3 and 4.
6. Look up your risk ratings on the Heart Disease Risk Rating Scale and record them in the Results section. Answer the questions in the Conclusions and Implications section.

Results: Write your risk scores and risk ratings in the appropriate boxes below.

Heart Disease Risk Scores and Ratings

	Score	Rating
Unalterable risk		
Alterable risk		
Total heart disease risk		

Heart Disease Risk Rating Chart

Rating	Unalterable Score	Alterable Score	Total Score
Very high	9 or more	21 or more	31 or more
High	7–8	15–20	26–30
Average	5–6	11–14	16–25
Low	4 or less	10 or less	15 or less

Conclusions and Implications: The higher your score on the Heart Disease Risk Factor Questionnaire, the greater your heart disease risk. In several sentences, discuss your risk for heart disease. Which of the risk factors do you need to control to reduce your risk for heart disease? Why?

Lab 5A Self-Assessment of Physical Activity

Name **Section** **Date**

Purpose: To estimate your current levels of physical activity from each category of the physical activity pyramid

Procedures

1. Place an X over the circle that characterizes your participation in each category in the pyramid. Place an X over one circle below the yellow box at the bottom of the pyramid to indicate days of inactivity.
2. Determine if you met the national goal for each type of activity. In the Results section of the chart on the next page, place an X over the "yes" circle if you meet the goal in each area or an X over the "no" circle if you do not meet the goal.

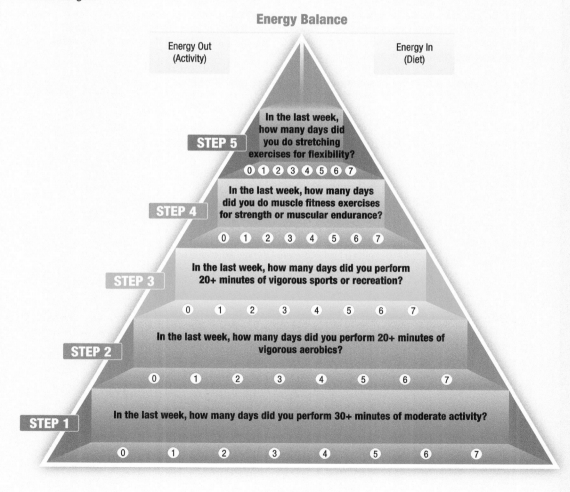

Energy Balance

Energy Out
(Activity)

Energy In
(Diet)

STEP 5 — In the last week, how many days did you do stretching exercises for flexibility?
0 1 2 3 4 5 6 7

STEP 4 — In the last week, how many days did you do muscle fitness exercises for strength or muscular endurance?
0 1 2 3 4 5 6 7

STEP 3 — In the last week, how many days did you perform 20+ minutes of vigorous sports or recreation?
0 1 2 3 4 5 6 7

STEP 2 — In the last week, how many days did you perform 20+ minutes of vigorous aerobics?
0 1 2 3 4 5 6 7

STEP 1 — In the last week, how many days did you perform 30+ minutes of moderate activity?
0 1 2 3 4 5 6 7

Inactivity

In the last week, how many days did you fail to do any activities from the 5 steps above?
0 1 2 3 4 5 6 7

Results

Activity Type	Step	National Goal	Did You Meet the National Health Goal?	
Moderate activity	1	5 days or more	Yes	No
Vigorous activity	2 and 3	3 days or more	Yes	No
Muscle fitness	4	2 days or more	Yes	No
Flexibility exercises	5	3 days or more	Yes	No
Inactivity	—	Avoid total inactivity	Yes	No

Conclusions and Implications: In the space below, write a brief paper describing your current physical activity patterns. Do you meet the national health goals in all areas? If not, in what types of activity from the pyramid do you need to improve? Are the answers you gave for the past week typical of your regular activity patterns? If you meet all national health goals, explain why you think this is so. Do you think that meeting the goals in the pyramid on the previous page indicates good activity patterns for you?

Write your physical activity assessment paper in the space below.

Lab 5B Estimating Your Fitness

Name		Section	Date

Purpose: To help you better understand each of the 11 components of health-related and skill-related physical fitness and to help you estimate your current levels of physical fitness

Special Note: The activities performed in the lab are *not intended as valid tests of physical fitness.* Completing the activities will help you better understand each component of fitness and help you estimate your current fitness levels. You should not rely primarily on the results of the activities to make your estimates. Rather, you should rely on previous fitness tests you have taken and your own best judgment of your current fitness. Later in this book, you will learn how to perform accurate assessments of each fitness component and determine the accuracy of your estimates.

Procedures

1. Consider a warm-up before and cool-down after. Perform each of the activities described in Chart 1 on page 100.
2. Use past fitness test performances and your own judgment to estimate your current levels for each of the health-related and skill-related physical fitness parts. Low fitness = improvement definitely needed, marginal fitness = some improvement necessary, good fitness = adequate for healthy daily living.
3. Place an X in the appropriate circle for your fitness estimate in the Results section.

Results

Fitness Component	Low Fitness	Marginal Fitness	Good Fitness
Balance	◯	◯	◯
Power	◯	◯	◯
Agility	◯	◯	◯
Reaction time	◯	◯	◯
Speed	◯	◯	◯
Coordination	◯	◯	◯
Cardiovascular fitness	◯	◯	◯
Flexibility	◯	◯	◯
Body composition	◯	◯	◯
Strength	◯	◯	◯
Muscular endurance	◯	◯	◯

Conclusions and Implications: In several sentences, discuss the information you used to make your estimates of physical fitness. How confident are you that these estimates are accurate?

Directions: Attempt each of the activities in Chart 1. Place an X in the circle next to each component of physical fitness to indicate that you have attempted the activity.

Chart 1 Physical Fitness Activities

Balance ⃝

1. *One-foot balance.* Stand on one foot; press up so that the weight is on the ball of the foot with the heel off the floor. Hold the hands and the other leg straight out in front for 10 seconds.

Power ⃝

2. *Standing long jump.* Stand with the toes behind a line. Using no run or hop step, jump as far as possible. Men must jump their height plus 6 inches. Women must jump their height only.

Agility ⃝

3. *Paper ball pickup.* Place two wadded paper balls on the floor 5 feet away. Run until both feet cross the line, pick up the first ball, and return both feet behind the starting line. Repeat with the second ball. Finish in 5 seconds.

Reaction Time ⃝

4. *Paper drop.* Have a partner hold a sheet of notebook paper so that the side edge is between your thumb and index finger, about the width of your hand from the top of the page. When your partner drops the paper, catch it before it slips through the thumb and finger. Do not lower your hand to catch the paper.

Speed ⃝

5. *Double-heel click.* With the feet apart, jump up and tap the heels together twice before you hit the ground. You must land with your feet at least 3 inches apart.

Coordination ⃝

6. *Paper ball bounce.* Wad up a sheet of notebook paper into a ball. Bounce the ball back and forth between the right and left hands. Keep the hands open and palms up. Bounce the ball three times with each hand (six times total), alternating hands for each bounce.

Cardiovascular Fitness ⃝

7. *Run in place.* Run in place for 1½ minutes (120 steps per minute). Rest for 1 minute and count the heart rate for 30 seconds. A heart rate of 60 (for 30 sec.) or lower passes. A step is counted each time the right foot hits the floor.

Flexibility ⃝

8. *Backsaver toe touch.* Sit on the floor with one foot against a wall. Bend the other knee. Bend forward at the hips. After three warm-up trials, reach forward and touch your closed fists to the wall. Bend forward slowly; do not bounce. Repeat with the other leg straight. Pass if fists touch the wall with each leg straight.

Body Composition ⃝

9. *The pinch.* Have a partner pinch a fold of fat on the back of your upper arm (body fatness), halfway between the tip of the elbow and the tip of the shoulder.

Men: no greater than 3/4 inch

Women: no greater than 1 inch

Strength ⃝

10. *Push-up.* Lie face down on the floor. Place the hands under the shoulders. Keeping the legs and body straight, press off the floor until the arms are fully extended. Women repeat once; men, three times.

Muscular Endurance ⃝

11. *Side leg raise.* Lie on the floor on your side. Lift your leg up and to the side of the body until your feet are 24 to 36 inches apart. Keep the knee and pelvis facing forward. Do not rotate so that the knees face the ceiling. Perform 10 with each leg.

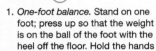

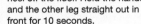

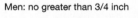

The Physical Activity Pyramid

Lab 6A Setting Goals for Moderate Physical Activity and Self-Monitoring (Logging) Program

Name	**Section**	**Date**

Purpose: To set moderate activity goals and to self-monitor (log) physical activity

Procedures

1. Read the five stages of change questions below. Place a check by the stage that best represents your current moderate physical activity level. If you are at stages 1–3 (precontemplation, contemplation, or preparation), you may want to set goals below the threshold of 30 minutes per day to get started. Those at the action or maintenance stage should consider goals of 30 minutes or more per day.
2. Determine moderate activity goals for each day of a 1-week period. In the columns (Chart 1) under the heading "Moderate Activity Goals," record the total minutes per day that you expect to perform **OR** the total steps per day that you expect to perform. Record the specific date for each day of the week in the "Date" column.
3. The goals should be realistic for you, but try to set goals that would meet current physical activity guidelines. If you choose step goals, you will need a pedometer. Use Table 4 on page 107 to help you to choose daily step goals.
4. If you choose minutes per day as your goals, use Chart 2 to keep track of the number of minutes of activity that you perform on each day of the 7-day period. Record the number of minutes for each bout of activity of at least 10 minutes in length performed during each day (Chart 2). Determine a total number of minutes for the day and record this total in the last column of Chart 2 and in the "Minutes Performed" column of Chart 1.
5. If you choose steps per day as your goals, determine the total steps per day accumulated on the pedometer and record that number of steps in the "Steps Performed" column for each day of the week (Chart 1).
6. Answer the questions in the Conclusions and Implications section (use full sentences for your answers).

Determine your stage for moderate physical activity. Check only the stage that represents your current moderate activity level.

☐ Precontemplation: I do not meet moderate activity guidelines and have not been thinking about starting.

☐ Contemplation: I do not meet moderate activity guidelines but have been thinking about starting.

☐ Preparation: I am planning to start doing regular moderate activity to meet guidelines.

☐ Action: I do moderate activity, but I am not as regular as I should be.

☐ Maintenance: I regularly meet national goals for moderate activity.

Chart 1 Moderate Physical Activity Goals and Summary Performance Log

Select a goal for each day in a 1-week plan. Keep a log of the activities performed to determine if your goals are met.

	Date:	Moderate Activity Goals		Summary Performance Log	
		Minutes/day	Steps/day	Minutes Performed	Steps Performed
Day 1					
Day 2					
Day 3					
Day 4					
Day 5					
Day 6					
Day 7					

Chart 2 Moderate Physical Activity Log (Daily Minutes Performed)

If you choose minutes per day as goals, write the number of minutes for each bout of moderate activity performed each day. Record a daily total (total minutes of moderate activity per day) in the "Daily Total" column. Record daily totals in Chart 1.

Moderate Activity Bouts of 10 Minutes or More

	Date	Bout 1	Bout 2	Bout 3	Bout 4	Bout 5	Daily Total
Day 1							
Day 2							
Day 3							
Day 4							
Day 5							
Day 6							
Day 7							

Did you meet your moderate activity goals for at least 5 days of the week?   (Yes) (No)

Do you think you can consistently meet your moderate activity goals?   (Yes) (No)

What activities did you perform most often when doing moderate activity?
List most common activities in the spaces below.

[ ] [ ]

[ ] [ ]

Conclusions and Interpretations

1. Do you feel that you will use moderate physical activity as a regular part of your lifetime physical activity plan, either now or in the future? Use several sentences to explain your answer.

[ ]

2. Did setting goals and logging activity make you more aware of your daily moderate physical activity patterns? Explain why or why not.

[ ]

Lab 6B Evaluating Physical Activity Environments

Name	Section	Date

Purpose: To help you assess community factors that may influence your ability to perform lifestyle physical activity

Procedures

1. Use the community audit forms on the next page to conduct an evaluation of the walkability of your community and the availability of community resources for physical activity. The walkability audit requires that you take a brief walk in your neighborhood to note key features in the environment that may help or hinder walking. The community audit will require you to evaluate the quality of resources and programming available in your community. You can choose your campus community or your hometown.
2. For each question, first use the check boxes to note the presence or absence of key features in the environment. Then base your score for this question on the number of checks and your overall perception.
3. After you have completed both the Walkability Audit and the Community Resource Audit, total the scores for each tool and report the total scores in the bottom. Add up both scores to compute the Combined (physical activity) Environmental Audit.

Results: Record your rating for each of three healthy lifestyles in the following chart.

Environmental Activity Scoring Chart	Score	Rating
Walkability Audit		
Community Resource Audit		
Combined Environmental Audit		

Rating Chart for Environmental Audits	Good	Marginal	Poor
Walkability	15–20	11–14	<11
Community	15–20	11–14	<11
Combined	30–40	22–29	<22

Conclusions and Implications

Provide a brief summary of the physical activity environment in your community. Describe your experiences in evaluating the walkability of and resources in your community. If the environment is close to ideal, comment on how this may facilitate active lifestyles. If the environment is not ideal, comment on what needs to be done to improve it.

Comments on Walkability Audit

Comments on Community Resource Audit

Lab 6B

Evaluating Physical Activity Environments

Walkability and Community Resource Audits

Directions. Place a check by each box in each questionnaire. Based on the number of boxes checked for each question, place an X over the circle to rate each question (1=poor, 2=marginal, 3=good, 4=very good). Add rating numbers to get walkability scores and community resource scores. Total the two to get a combined environmental score.

Walkability Audit   **Rating**

1. Did you have room to walk?   ① ② ③ ④
   - ☐ Sidewalks blocked or not continuous
   - ☐ Sidewalks were broken, cracked
   - ☐ No sidewalks, paths, or shoulders
   - ☐ Too much traffic on sidewalk
   - ☐ Other _____

2. Was it easy to cross streets?   ① ② ③ ④
   - ☐ Road was too wide
   - ☐ Traffic signals were too short/too long
   - ☐ Parked cars blocked view of street
   - ☐ No striped or designated crosswalks
   - ☐ Other _____

3. Was it safe for walking?   ① ② ③ ④
   - ☐ Too much traffic
   - ☐ Drivers too fast/too close
   - ☐ Inadequate lighting
   - ☐ Area of high crime
   - ☐ Other _____

4. Were there places to go?   ① ② ③ ④
   - ☐ No stores in the area
   - ☐ No restaurants in the area
   - ☐ No friends nearby
   - ☐ Nothing interesting to see in area
   - ☐ Other _____

5. Was your walk pleasant?   ① ② ③ ④
   - ☐ Not enough grass and trees
   - ☐ Scary dogs or people
   - ☐ Not well lighted
   - ☐ Too dirty
   - ☐ Other _____

Community Resource Audit   **Rating**

6. Are there walking/biking paths in the area?   ① ② ③ ④
   - ☐ Paths are in unsafe areas
   - ☐ Paths need to be repaired
   - ☐ Paths are too crowded
   - ☐ Paths are too far away to be useful
   - ☐ Other _____

7. Is there a community fitness/rec center?   ① ② ③ ④
   - ☐ Center is too expensive
   - ☐ Center is not clean or updated
   - ☐ Center is too far away
   - ☐ Center has old or limited equipment
   - ☐ Other _____

8. Are there bicycle lanes on streets?   ① ② ③ ④
   - ☐ Lines not painted well
   - ☐ Lines not on all streets
   - ☐ Bike lanes not wide enough
   - ☐ Cars too close
   - ☐ Other _____

9. Are there parks, fields, and playgrounds?   ① ② ③ ④
   - ☐ Parks in unsafe areas
   - ☐ Equipment/resources in poor repair
   - ☐ Too crowded
   - ☐ Too far away
   - ☐ Other _____

10. Are there community activity programs?   ① ② ③ ④
    - ☐ Not enough programs
    - ☐ Not the right type of programs
    - ☐ Too expensive
    - ☐ Too far/inconvenient
    - ☐ Other _____

Total Score for Walkability Audit: ☐ (Sum of Questions 1–5)

Total Score for Community Resources Audit: ☐ (Sum of Questions 6–10)

Combined Environmental Audit: ☐ (Sum of Questions 1–10)

> Walkability checklist adapted from resources developed by the Partnership for a Walkable America. For information on this organization, visit this website: **www.walkableamerica.org**.

Lab Resource Materials: Evaluating Cardiovascular Fitness

The Walking Test

- Warm up; then walk 1 mile as fast as you can without straining. Record your time to the nearest second.
- Immediately after the walk, count your heart rate for 15 seconds; then multiply by four to get a 1-minute heart rate. Record your heart rate.
- Use your walking time and your postexercise heart rate to determine your rating using Chart 1.

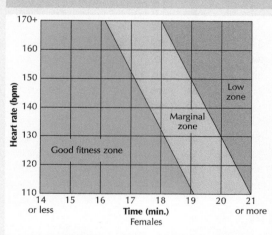

Chart 1 Walking Ratings for Males and Females

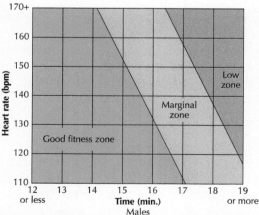

Source: James M. Rippe, M.D.

The ratings in Chart 1 are for ages 20 to 29. They provide reasonable ratings for people of all ages.

Note: The walking test is not a good indicator of high performance; the running and bicycle tests are recommended.

Step Test

- Step up and down on a 12-inch bench for 3 minutes at a rate of 24 steps per minute. One step consists of four beats—that is, "up with the left foot, up with the right foot, down with the left foot, down with the right foot."
- Immediately after the exercise, sit down on the bench and relax. Don't talk.
- Locate your pulse or have someone locate it for you.
- Five seconds after the exercise ends, begin counting your pulse. Count the pulse for 60 seconds.
- Your score is your 60-second heart rate. Locate your score and your rating on Chart 2.

Chart 2 Step Test Rating Chart

Classification	60-Second Heart Rate
High-performance zone	84 or less
Good fitness zone	85–95
Marginal zone	96–119
Low zone	120 and above

Source: Kasch and Boyer.

As you grow older, you will want to continue to score well on this rating chart. Because your maximal heart rate decreases as you age, you should be able to score well if you exercise regularly.

The Astrand-Ryhming Bicycle Test

- Ride a stationary bicycle ergometer for 6 minutes at a rate of 50 pedal cycles per minute (one push with each foot per cycle). Cool down after the test.
- Set the bicycle at a workload between 300 and 1,200 kpm. For less fit or smaller people, a setting in the range of 300 to 600 is appropriate. Larger or fitter people will need to use a setting of 750 to 1,200. The workload should be enough to elevate the heart rate to at least 125 bpm but no more than 170 bpm during the ride. The ideal range is 140–150 bpm.
- During the sixth minute of the ride (if the heart rate is in the correct range—see previous step), count the heart rate for the entire sixth minute. The carotid or radial pulse may be used.
- Use Chart 3 (males) or 4 (females) to determine your predicted oxygen uptake score in liters per minute. Locate your heart rate for the sixth minute of the ride in the left column and the work rate in kp·m/min. across the top. The number in the chart where the heart rate and work rate intersect represents your predicted O_2 uptake in liters per minute. The bicycle you use must allow you to easily and accurately determine the work rate in kp·m/min.

- Ratings are typically assigned based on milliliters per kilogram of body weight per minute. To convert your score to milliliters per kilogram per minute (mL/kg/min.), the first step is to multiply your score from Chart 3 or 4 by 1,000. This converts your score from liters to milliliters. Then divide your weight in pounds by 2.2. This converts your weight to kilograms. Then divide your score in milliliters by your weight in kilograms. This gives you your score in mL/kg/min.

- Example: An oxygen uptake score of 3.5 liters is equal to a 3,500-milliliter score (3.5 × 1,000). If the person with this score weighed 150 pounds, his or her weight in kilograms would be 68.18 kilograms (150 divided by 2.2). The person's oxygen uptake would be 51.3 mL/kg/min. (3,500 divided by 68.18).

- Use your score in mL/kg/min. to determine your rating (Chart 5).

Chart 3 Determining Oxygen Uptake Using the Bicycle Test—Men (Liters O_2/min.)

Heart Rate	450	600	900	1,200	Heart Rate	450	600	900	1,200	1,500	Heart Rate	450	600	900	1,200	1,500
123	3.3	3.4	4.6	6.0	139	2.5	2.6	3.6	4.8	6.0	155	2.0	2.2	3.0	4.0	5.0
124	3.3	3.3	4.5	6.0	140	2.5	2.6	3.6	4.8	6.0	156	1.9	2.2	2.9	4.0	5.0
125	3.2	3.2	4.4	5.9	141	2.4	2.6	3.5	4.7	5.9	157	1.9	2.1	2.9	3.9	4.9
126	3.1	3.2	4.4	5.8	142	2.4	2.5	3.5	4.6	5.8	158	1.8	2.1	2.9	3.9	4.9
127	3.0	3.1	4.3	5.7	143	2.4	2.5	3.4	4.6	5.7	159	1.8	2.1	2.8	3.8	4.8
128	3.0	3.1	4.2	5.6	144	2.3	2.5	3.4	4.5	5.7	160	1.8	2.1	2.8	3.8	4.8
129	2.9	3.0	4.2	5.6	145	2.3	2.4	3.4	4.5	5.6	161	1.7	2.0	2.8	3.7	4.7
130	2.9	3.0	4.1	5.5	146	2.3	2.4	3.3	4.4	5.6	162	1.7	2.0	2.8	3.7	4.6
131	2.8	2.9	4.0	5.4	147	2.3	2.4	3.3	4.4	5.5	163	1.7	2.0	2.8	3.7	4.6
132	2.8	2.9	4.0	5.3	148	2.2	2.4	3.2	4.3	5.4	164	1.6	2.0	2.7	3.6	4.5
133	2.7	2.8	3.9	5.3	149	2.2	2.3	3.2	4.3	5.4	165	1.6	1.9	2.7	3.6	4.5
134	2.7	2.8	3.9	5.2	150	2.2	2.3	3.2	4.2	5.3	166	1.6	1.9	2.7	3.6	4.5
135	2.7	2.8	3.8	5.1	151	2.2	2.3	3.1	4.2	5.2	167	1.5	1.9	2.6	3.5	4.4
136	2.6	2.7	3.8	5.0	152	2.1	2.3	3.1	4.1	5.2	168	1.5	1.9	2.6	3.5	4.4
137	2.6	2.7	3.7	5.0	153	2.1	2.2	3.0	4.1	5.1	169	1.5	1.9	2.6	3.5	4.3
138	2.5	2.7	3.7	4.9	154	2.0	2.2	3.0	4.0	5.1	170	1.4	1.8	2.6	3.4	4.3

Chart 4 Determining Oxygen Uptake Using the Bicycle Test—Women (Liters O_2/min.)

Heart Rate	300	450	600	750	900	Heart Rate	300	450	600	750	900	Heart Rate	400	600	750	900
123	2.4	3.1	3.9	4.6	5.1	139	1.8	2.4	2.9	3.5	4.0	155	1.9	2.4	2.8	3.2
124	2.4	3.1	3.8	4.5	5.1	140	1.8	2.4	2.8	3.4	4.0	156	1.9	2.4	2.8	3.2
125	2.3	3.0	3.7	4.4	5.0	141	1.8	2.3	2.8	3.4	3.9	157	1.8	2.3	2.7	3.2
126	2.3	3.0	3.6	4.3	5.0	142	1.7	2.3	2.8	3.3	3.9	158	1.8	2.3	2.7	3.1
127	2.2	2.9	3.5	4.2	4.8	143	1.7	2.2	2.7	3.3	3.8	159	1.8	2.3	2.7	3.1
128	2.2	2.8	3.5	4.2	4.8	144	1.7	2.2	2.7	3.2	3.8	160	1.8	2.2	2.6	3.0
129	2.2	2.8	3.4	4.1	4.8	145	1.6	2.2	2.7	3.2	3.7	161	1.8	2.2	2.6	3.0
130	2.1	2.7	3.4	4.0	4.7	146	1.6	2.2	2.6	3.2	3.7	162	1.8	2.2	2.6	3.0
131	2.1	2.7	3.4	4.0	4.6	147	1.6	2.1	2.6	3.1	3.6	163	1.7	2.2	2.5	2.9
132	2.0	2.7	3.3	3.9	4.6	148	1.6	2.1	2.6	3.1	3.6	164	1.7	2.1	2.5	2.9
133	2.0	2.6	3.2	3.8	4.5	149	1.5	2.1	2.6	3.0	3.5	165	1.7	2.1	2.5	2.9
134	2.0	2.6	3.2	3.8	4.4	150	1.5	2.0	2.5	3.0	3.5	166	1.7	2.1	2.5	2.8
135	2.0	2.6	3.1	3.7	4.4	151	1.5	2.0	2.5	3.0	3.4	167	1.6	2.0	2.4	2.8
136	1.9	2.5	3.1	3.6	4.3	152	1.4	2.0	2.5	2.9	3.4	168	1.6	2.0	2.4	2.8
137	1.9	2.5	3.0	3.6	4.2	153	1.4	2.0	2.4	2.9	3.3	169	1.6	2.0	2.4	2.8
138	1.8	2.4	3.0	3.5	4.2	154	1.4	2.0	2.4	2.8	3.3	170	1.6	2.0	2.4	2.7

Chart 5 Bicycle Test Rating Scale (mL/O₂/kg/min.)

	Men				
Age	17–26	27–39	40–49	50–59	60–69
High-performance zone	50+	46+	42+	39+	35+
Good fitness zone	43–49	35–45	32–41	29–38	26–34
Marginal zone	35–42	30–34	27–31	25–28	22–25
Low zone	<35	<30	<27	<25	<22

	Women				
Age	17–26	27–39	40–49	50–59	60–69
High-performance zone	46+	40+	38+	35+	32+
Good fitness zone	36–45	33–39	30–37	28–34	24–31
Marginal zone	30–35	28–32	24–29	21–27	18–23
Low zone	<30	<28	<24	<21	<18

The 12-Minute Run Test

- Locate an area where a specific distance is already marked, such as a school track or football field, or measure a specific distance using a bicycle or automobile odometer.
- Use a stopwatch or wristwatch to accurately time a 12-minute period.

- For best results, warm up prior to the test; then run at a steady pace for the entire 12 minutes (cool down after the test).
- Determine the distance you can run in 12 minutes in fractions of a mile. Depending upon your age, locate your score and rating in Chart 6.

Chart 6 Twelve-Minute Run Test Rating Chart

	Men (Age)							
	17–26		27–39		40–49		50+	
Classification—Men	Miles	Km	Miles	Km	Miles	Km	Miles	Km
High-performance zone	1.80+	2.90+	1.60+	2.60+	1.50+	2.40+	1.40+	2.25+
Good fitness zone	1.55–1.79	2.50–2.89	1.45–1.59	2.35–2.59	1.40–1.49	2.25–2.39	1.25–1.39	2.00–2.24
Marginal zone	1.35–1.54	2.20–2.49	1.30–1.44	2.10–2.34	1.25–1.39	2.00–2.24	1.10–1.24	1.75–1.99
Low zone	<1.35	<2.20	<1.30	<2.10	<1.25	<2.00	<1.1	<1.75

	Women (Age)							
	17–26		27–39		40–49		50+	
Classification—Women	Miles	Km	Miles	Km	Miles	Km	Miles	Km
High-performance zone	1.45+	2.35+	1.35+	2.20+	1.25+	2.00+	1.15+	1.85+
Good fitness zone	1.25–1.44	2.00–2.34	2.20–1.34	1.95–2.19	1.15–1.24	1.85–1.99	1.05–1.14	1.70–1.84
Marginal zone	1.15–1.24	1.85–1.99	1.05–1.19	1.70–1.94	1.00–1.14	1.60–1.84	.95–1.04	1.55–1.69
Low zone	<1.15	<1.85	<1.05	<1.70	<1.00	<1.60	<.95	<1.55

Source: Based on data from Cooper.

Evaluating Cardiovascular Fitness

The 12-Minute Swim Test

- Locate a swimming area with premeasured distances, preferably 20 yards or longer.
- After a warm-up, swim as far as possible in 12 minutes using the stroke of your choice.

- For best results, have a partner keep track of your time and distance. A degree of swimming competence is a prerequisite for this test.
- Determine your score and rating using Chart 7.

Chart 7 Twelve-Minute Swim Rating Chart

| | Men (Age) | | | | | | | |
| | 17–26 | | 27–39 | | 40–49 | | 50+ | |
Classification—Men	Yards	Meters	Yards	Meters	Yards	Meters	Yards	Meters
High-performance zone	700+	650+	650+	600+	600+	550+	550+	500+
Good fitness zone	600–699	550–649	550–649	500–599	500–599	475–549	450–549	425–499
Marginal zone	500–599	450–549	450–459	400–499	400–499	375–475	350–449	325–424
Low zone	Below 500	Below 450	Below 450	Below 400	Below 400	Below 375	Below 350	Below 325

| | Women (Age) | | | | | | | |
| | 17–26 | | 27–39 | | 40–49 | | 50+ | |
Classification—Women	Yards	Meters	Yards	Meters	Yards	Meters	Yards	Meters
High-performance zone	600+	550+	550+	500+	500+	450+	450+	400+
Good fitness zone	500–599	450–549	450–549	400–499	400–499	375–449	350–449	325–400
Marginal zone	400–499	350–449	350–449	325–399	300–399	275–375	250–349	225–324
Low zone	Below 400	Below 350	Below 350	Below 325	Below 300	Below 275	Below 250	Below 225

Source: Based on data from Cooper.

Chart 8 Non-Exercise Fitness Assessment Rating Chart

Rating	Score
Needs Improvement	1–4
Marginal	5–9
Good Conditioning	10–13
Highly Conditioned	13+

Lab 7A Counting Target Heart Rate and Ratings of Perceived Exertion

Name	**Section**	**Date**

Purpose: To learn to count heart rate accurately and to use heart rate and/or ratings of perceived exertion (RPE) to establish the threshold of training and target zones

Procedure

1. Practice counting the number of pulses felt for a given period of time at both the carotid and radial locations. Use a clock or watch to count for 15, 30, and 60 seconds. To establish your heart rate in beats per minute, multiply your 15-second pulse by four, and your 30-second pulse by two.
2. Practice locating your carotid and radial pulses quickly. This is important when trying to count your pulse after exercise.
3. Run a quarter mile; then count your heart rate at the end of the run. Try to run at a rate you think will keep the rate of the heart above the threshold of training and in the target zone. Use 15-second pulse counts (choose either carotid or radial) and multiply by four to get heart rate in beats per minute (bpm). Record the bpm in the Results section.
4. Rate your perceived exertion (RPE) for the run (see RPE chart below). Record your results.
5. Repeat the run a second time. Try to run at a speed that gets you in the heart rate and RPE target zone. Record your heart rate and RPE results.

Results: Record your *resting* heart rates in the boxes below.

Carotid Pulse | **Heart Rate per Minute** | **Radial Pulse** | **Heart Rate per Minute**

15 seconds × 4 =

30 seconds × 2 =

60 seconds × 1 =

15 seconds × 4 =

30 seconds × 2 =

60 seconds × 1 =

Record your heart rate and rating of perceived exertion for run 1.

Pulse Count | **Heart Rate per Minute**

15 seconds × 4 =

Rating of Perceived Exertion

Record your heart rate and rating of perceived exertion for run 2.

Pulse Count | **Heart Rate per Minute**

15 seconds × 4 =

Rating of Perceived Exertion

Ratings of Perceived Exertion (RPE)	
Rating	**Description**
6	
7	Very, very light
8	
9	Very light
10	
11	Fairly light
12	
13	Somewhat hard
14	
15	Hard
16	
17	Very hard
18	
19	Very, very hard
20	

Source: Data from Borg, G.

Lab 7A

Counting Target Heart Rate and Ratings of Perceived Exertion

Answer the following questions:

Which pulse-counting technique did you use after the runs?   Carotid ◯   Radial ◯

What is your heart rate target zone (to calculate, see pages 125 and 126) [_____] bpm

Was your heart rate for run 1 enough to get in the heart rate target zone?   Yes ◯   No ◯

Was your RPE for run 1 enough to get in the target zone (12–16)?   Yes ◯   No ◯

Was your heart rate for run 2 enough to get in the heart rate target zone?   Yes ◯   No ◯

Was your RPE for run 2 enough to get in the target zone (12–16)?   Yes ◯   No ◯

Conclusions and Implications: In several sentences, discuss your results, including which method you would use to count heart rate and why. Also discuss heart rate versus RPE (Rating of Perceived Exertion) for determining the target zone.

Lab Supplement:* You may want to keep track of your exercise heart rate over a week's time or longer to see if you are reaching the target zone in your workouts. Shade your target zone with a highlight pen and plot your exercise heart rate for each day of the week (see sample).

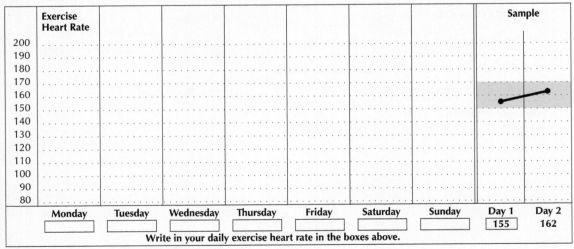

*Thanks to Ginnie Atkins for suggesting this lab supplement.

Lab 7B Evaluating Cardiovascular Fitness

Name		Section	Date

Purpose: To acquaint you with several methods for evaluating cardiovascular fitness and to help you evaluate and rate your own cardiovascular fitness

Procedure

1. Perform one or more of the four cardiovascular fitness tests and determine your ratings using the information in the Lab Resource Materials.
2. Perform each of the four steps for the Non-Exercise Estimate of Cardiovascular Fitness using the information on the back of this page. Learning this technique will allow you to estimate your fitness when you are injured or for some other reason cannot do a performance test.

Results

1. Record the information from your cardiovascular fitness test(s) in the spaces provided.
2. After you have completed the four steps for the Non-Exercise Estimate of Cardiovascular Fitness, use Chart 8 in Lab Resource Materials (page 134) to determine your fitness rating.

Walking Test

Time		minutes
Heart rate		bpm
Rating		(see Chart 1, page 131)

Bicycle Test

Workload		kpm
Heart rate		bpm
Weight		pounds
Weight in kg*		
mL/O$_2$/kg		
Rating		(see Chart 5, page 133)

Non-Exercise Test

| Score | | |
| Rating | | (see Chart 8, page 134) |

Step Test

| Heart rate | | bpm |
| Rating | | (see Chart 2, page 131) |

12-Minute Run Test

| Distance | | miles |
| Rating | | (see Chart 6, page 133) |

12-Minute Swim Test

| Distance | | yards |
| Rating | | (see Chart 7, page 134) |

*Weight in lb. ÷ 2.2.

Lab 7B

Evaluating Cardiovascular Fitness

Non-Exercise Cardiovascular Fitness Rating

Record your scores and do the calculations to determine scores for A to E below.

- Look up your activity score on Chart 1 (below). Record score in box A.   [   ] (A)

- Record your gender (female = 0/male = 1)   _____ $\times$ 2.77 = [   ] (B)

- Determine your resting heart rate (Lab 7A), record here   _____ $\times$ 0.03 = [   ] (C)

- Calculate your BMI (see Lab 13B), record here   _____ $\times$ 0.17 = [   ] (D)

- Record your age in years.   _____ $\times$ 0.10 = [   ] (E)

Use the following formula to calculate your score. Use Chart 8 on page 134 to get your rating.

18.07	+	A	+	B	–	C	–	D	–	E	=	Estimated Cardiovascular Fitness (METs)
18.07	+	[ ]	+	[ ]	–	[ ]	–	[ ]	–	[ ]	=	[ ]

Chart 1 Self-Reported Activity Score (for Step 1 Above)

Activity Score	Choose the Score That Best Describes Your Physical Activity Level
0.00	I am inactive or do little activity other than usual daily activities.
0.32	I regularly (> 5 d/wk) participate in physical activities requiring low levels of exertion that result in slight increases in breathing and heart rate for at least **10 minutes** at a time.
1.06	I participate in aerobic exercises such as brisk walking, jogging, or running, cycling, swimming, or vigorous sports at a comfortable pace, or activities requiring similar levels of exertion for **20 to 60 minutes per week.**
1.76	I participate in aerobic exercises such as brisk walking, jogging, or running at a comfortable pace, or other activities requiring similar levels of exertion for **1 to 3 hours per week.**
3.03	I participate in aerobic exercises such as brisk walking, jogging, or running at a comfortable pace, or other activities requiring similar levels of exertion for **over 3 hours per week.**

Conclusions and Implications

1. In several sentences, explain why you selected the tests you selected. Discuss your current level of cardiovascular fitness and steps you will need to take to maintain or improve it. Comment on the effectiveness of the tests you selected.

2. In several sentences, explain your results from the non-exercise assessment by comparing the results with the other test(s). Did the self-report version classify you into the same fitness category? Try to explain any differences you noted.

Lab 8A The Physical Activity Adherence Questionnaire

Name	Section	Date

Purpose: To help you understand the factors that influence physical activity adherence and to see which factors you might change to improve your chances of achieving the action or maintenance level for physical activity

Procedures

1. The factors that predispose, enable, and reinforce adherence to physically active living are listed below. Read each statement. Place an X in the circle under the most appropriate response for you: very true, somewhat true, or not true.
2. When you have answered all of the items, determine a score by summing the four numbers for each type of factor. Then sum the three scores (predisposing, enabling, reinforcing) to get your total score.
3. Record your scores in the Results section and answer the questions in the Conclusions and Implications section.

	Very True	Somewhat True	Not True	
Predisposing Factors				
1. I am very knowledgeable about physical activity.	3	2	1	
2. I have a strong belief that physical activity is good for me.	3	2	1	
3. I enjoy doing regular exercise and physical activity.	3	2	1	
4. I am confident of my abilities in sports, exercise, and other physical activities.	3	2	1	
Predisposing Score =				
Enabling Factors				
5. I possess good sports skills.	3	2	1	
6. I know how to plan my own physical activity program.	3	2	1	
7. I have a place to do physical activity near my home or work.	3	2	1	
8. I have the equipment I need to do physical activities I enjoy.	3	2	1	
Enabling Score =				
Reinforcing Factors				
9. I have the support of my family for doing my regular physical activity.	3	2	1	
10. I have many friends who enjoy the same kinds of physical activities that I do.	3	2	1	
11. I have the support of my boss and my colleagues for participation in activity.	3	2	1	
12. I have a doctor and/or an employer who encourages me to exercise.	3	2	1	
Reinforcing Score =				
Total Score (Sum 3 Scores) =				

Results: Record your scores in the "Score" column. Use your score and the Physical Activity Adherence Rating Chart to determine your ratings. Record your ratings in the "Rating" column below.

Physical Activity Adherence Ratings

Adherence Category	Score	Rating
Predisposing		
Enabling		
Reinforcing		
Total		

Physical Activity Adherence Ratings Chart

Classification	Predisposing Score	Enabling Score	Reinforcing Score	Total Score
Adherence likely	11–12	11–12	11–12	33–36
Adherence possible	9–10	9–10	9–10	25–32
Adherence unlikely	<9	<9	<9	<25

Conclusions and Implications: In several sentences, discuss your ratings from this questionnaire. Also discuss the predisposing, enabling, and reinforcing factors you may need to alter in order to increase your prospects for lifetime activity.

In several sentences, discuss what type of activity you find most enjoyable (vigorous aerobics, vigorous recreation, or vigorous sports). Comment on *why* you enjoy the activities that you have selected.

Lab 8B Planning and Logging Participation in Vigorous Physical Activity

Name	**Section**	**Date**

Purpose: To set 1-week vigorous physical activity goals, to prepare a plan, and to self-monitor progress in your 1-week vigorous aerobics, vigorous sports, and recreation plan

Procedures

1. Consider your current stage of change for vigorous activity using the questions provided below. Read the five stages of change questions below and place a check by the stage that best represents your current vigorous physical activity level.
2. Determine vigorous activity (active aerobics, active sports, or active recreation) goals for each day of a 1-week period. In the columns (Chart 1) under the heading "Vigorous Activity Goals," record the total minutes per day that you expect to perform. Record the specific date for each day of the week in the "Date" column and the activity or activities that you expect to perform in the "Activity" column.
3. Only bouts of 10 minutes or longer should be considered when selecting your daily minutes goals. The daily goals should be at least 20 minutes a day in the target zone for vigorous activity for at least 3 days of the week.
4. Use Chart 2 to keep track of the number of minutes of activity that you perform on each day of the 7-day period. Record the number of minutes for each bout of activity of at least 10 minutes in length performed during each day in Chart 2. Determine a total number of minutes for the day and record this total in the last column of Chart 2 and in the "minutes performed" column of Chart 1.
5. After completing Charts 1 and 2, answer the questions and complete the Conclusions and Implications section (use full sentences for your answers).

Determine your stage for vigorous physical activity. Check only the stage that represents your current vigorous activity level.

☐ Precontemplation. I do not meet vigorous activity guidelines and have not been thinking about starting.

☐ Contemplation. I do not do vigorous activity guidelines but have been thinking about starting.

☐ Preparation. I am planning to start doing regular vigorous activity to meet guidelines.

☐ Action. I do vigorous activity, but I am not as regular as I should be.

☐ Maintenance. I regularly meet national goals for vigorous activity.

Results

Chart 1 Vigorous Physical Activity Goals and Summary Performance Log

Select a goal for each day in a 1-week plan. Keep a log of the activities performed to determine if your goals are met (see Chart 2), and record total minutes performed in the chart below.

	Date	Vigorous Activity Goals		Summary Performance Log Total Minutes Peformed/Day
		Minutes/Day	Activity	
Day 1				
Day 2				
Day 3				
Day 4				
Day 5				
Day 6				
Day 7				

Chart 2 Vigorous Physical Activity Log (Daily Minutes Performed)

Record the number of minutes for each bout of vigorous activities performed each day. Add the minutes in each column for the day and record a daily total (total minutes of vigorous activity per day) in the "Daily Total" column. Record your daily totals in the last column of Chart 1.

| | Date | Vigorous Activity Bouts of 10 Minutes or More | | | | | Daily Total |
		Bout 1	Bout 2	Bout 3	Bout 4	Bout 5	
Day 1							
Day 2							
Day 3							
Day 4							
Day 5							
Day 6							
Day 7							

Did you meet your vigorous activity goals for at least 3 days of the week?   Yes   No

Do you think that you can consistently meet your vigorous activity goals?   Yes   No

What activities did you perform most often when doing vigorous activity?
List the most common activities that you performed in the spaces below.

Vigorous Aerobics	Vigorous Sports	Vigorous Recreation
_____	_____	_____
_____	_____	_____
_____	_____	_____

Conclusions and Interpretations

Are the activities that you listed above ones that you think you will perform regularly in the future?   Yes   No

Did setting goals and logging activity make you more aware of your daily vigorous physical activity patterns? Explain why or why not.

Lab 8C Combining Moderate and Vigorous Physical Activity

Name · Section · Date

Purpose: To learn about MET-minutes and how to combine moderate and vigorous physical activity to meet physical activity guidelines and goals

Procedures

1. National guidelines recommend at least 150 minutes of moderate or 75 minutes of vigorous physical activity as the minimum amount per week. The guidelines indicate that you can combine the two forms to meet your activity goal. When combining moderate and vigorous activities, MET-minutes are used. The minimum goal for beginners is 500 MET-minutes and 1,000 MET-minutes is the minimum goal for a reasonably fit and active person. Consider this information as you complete the rest of this lab.
2. In Chart 1 below list several moderate activities and several vigorous activities for each day of one week. Next to the activities indicate the number of minutes you plan to perform each activity. Be sure to choose both moderate and vigorous activities.
3. Use the information in Chart 2 to determine a MET value for each activity or use the compendium of activities website to determine values for those not listed in Chart 2. Record the MET value in the space provided for each activity.
4. Multiply the MET values for each activity by the number of minutes you plan to perform each activity to determine MET-minutes for each activity.
5. Total the MET-minute columns for both moderate and vigorous activities to be performed during the week.
6. Answer the questions in the Conclusions and Implications Section.

Results

Chart 1 Moderate and vigorous activity plan for one week

Day	Date	Moderate Activity Activity	Min.	METs	MET-min.	Vigorous Activity Activity	Min.	METS	MET-min.
1									
2									
3									
4									
5									
6									
7									
Totals							+		=

Total MET-minutes for the Week

Did you meet the 500 MET-minute recommendation for beginners? (Yes) (No)

Did you meet the 1,000 MET-minute recommendation for more active people? (Yes) (No)

Which is your weekly activity plan most likely to include?

☐ Moderate activity only

☐ Vigorous activity only

☐ Both moderate and vigorous activity

Chart 2 MET Values for Selected Moderate and Vigorous Physical Activities

Moderate Activities	METs	Vigorous Activities	METs
Vacuuming/Mopping	3.0	Shoveling Snow	6.0
Walking (3 mph)	3.0	Walking (4.5 mph)	6.3
Bowling	3.0	Aerobic Dance	6.5
Child Care	3.5	Bricklaying	7.0
Golf (riding)	3.5	Cross-Country Skiing (leisure)	7.0
Biking (10 mph flat)	4.0	Soccer (leisure)	7.0
Fishing (moving, not stationary)	4.0	Basketball (game)	8.0
Raking Leaves	4.0	Biking (12–17 mph)	8.0
Table Tennis	4.0	Hiking Terrain (pack)	8.0
Volleyball (non-comp.)	4.0	Jogging (5 mph)	8.0
Waitress	4.0	Tennis (singles)	8.0
Ballroom (social)	4.5	Volleyball (games)	8.0
Basketball (shooting)	4.5	Step Aerobics	8.5
Mowing Lawn (power)	4.5	Digging Ditches	8.5
Painting	4.5	Cross-Country Skiing (fast-5–7 mph)	9.0
Tennis Doubles	5.0	Swimming Laps (varies with strokes)	9.0
Walking (4 mph)	5.0	Jogging (6 mph)	10.0
Construction	5.5	Racquetball (games)	10.0
Farming	5.5	Soccer (competitive)	10.0
Golf (walking)	5.5	Running (11.5 mph)	11.5
Softball (games)	5.5	Handball (games)	12.0
Swimming (leisure)	5.5		

MET values based on the Compendium of Physical Activities (available at **http://prevention.sph.sc.edu/tools/docs/documents_compendium.pdf).**

Conclusions and Implications: In the space provided below discuss the MET-minute method of combining activities to meet goals. Do you think that this method will be useful to you? Explain why or why not using full sentences.

Lab Resource Materials

Muscles in the Body

Lab Resource Materials: Muscles in the Body

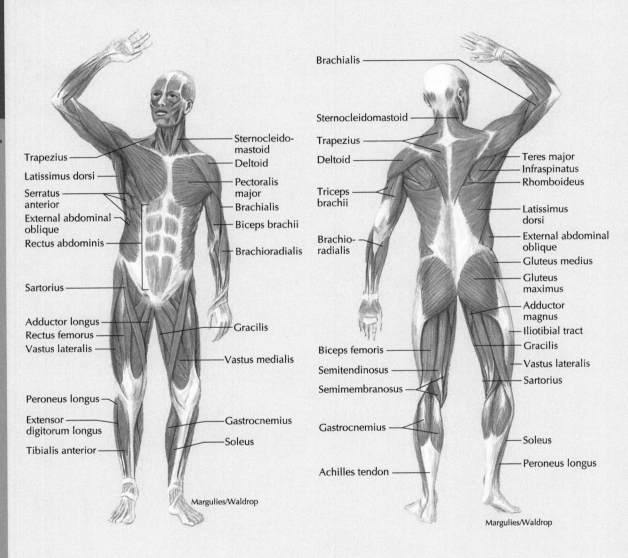

Trapezius
Latissimus dorsi
Serratus anterior
External abdominal oblique
Rectus abdominis
Sartorius
Adductor longus
Rectus femorus
Vastus lateralis
Peroneus longus
Extensor digitorum longus
Tibialis anterior

Sternocleido-mastoid
Deltoid
Pectoralis major
Brachialis
Biceps brachii
Brachioradialis
Gracilis
Vastus medialis
Gastrocnemius
Soleus

Margulies/Waldrop

Brachialis
Sternocleidomastoid
Trapezius
Deltoid
Triceps brachii
Brachio-radialis
Biceps femoris
Semitendinosus
Semimembranosus
Gastrocnemius
Achilles tendon

Teres major
Infraspinatus
Rhomboideus
Latissimus dorsi
External abdominal oblique
Gluteus medius
Gluteus maximus
Adductor magnus
Iliotibial tract
Gracilis
Vastus lateralis
Sartorius
Soleus
Peroneus longus

Margulies/Waldrop

Lab Resource Materials: Muscle Fitness Tests

Evaluating Isotonic Strength: 1RM

1. Use a weight machine for the leg press and seated arm press (or bench press) for the evaluation.
2. Estimate how much weight you can lift two or three times. Be conservative; it is better to start with too little weight than too much. If you lift the weight more than 10 times, the procedure should be done again on another day when you are rested.
3. Using correct form, perform a leg press with the weight you have chosen. Perform as many times as you can up to 10.
4. Use Chart 1 to determine your 1RM for the leg press. Find the weight used in the left-hand column and then find the number of repetitions you performed across the top of the chart.
5. Your 1RM score is the value where the weight row and the repetitions column intersect.
6. Repeat this procedure for the seated arm press.
7. Record your 1RM scores for the leg press and seated arm press in the Results section on page 191.
8. Next, divide your 1RM scores by your body weight in pounds to get a "strength per pound of body weight" (str/lb./body wt.) score for each of the two exercises.
9. Finally, determine your strength rating for your upper body strength (arm press) and lower body (leg press) using Chart 2 (page 188).

Chart 1 Predicted 1RM Based on Reps-to-Fatigue

Wt.	Repetitions										Wt.	Repetitions									
	1	2	3	4	5	6	7	8	9	10		1	2	3	4	5	6	7	8	9	10
30	30	31	32	33	34	35	36	37	38	39	170	170	175	180	185	191	197	204	211	219	227
35	35	37	38	39	40	41	42	43	44	45	175	175	180	185	191	197	203	210	217	225	233
40	40	41	42	44	46	47	49	50	51	53	180	180	185	191	196	202	209	216	223	231	240
45	45	46	48	49	51	52	54	56	58	60	185	185	190	196	202	208	215	222	230	238	247
50	50	51	53	55	56	58	60	62	64	67	190	190	195	201	207	214	221	228	236	244	253
55	55	57	58	60	62	64	66	68	71	73	195	195	201	206	213	219	226	234	242	251	260
60	60	62	64	65	67	70	72	74	77	80	200	200	206	212	218	225	232	240	248	257	267
65	65	67	69	71	73	75	78	81	84	87	205	205	211	217	224	231	238	246	254	264	273
70	70	72	74	76	79	81	84	87	90	93	210	210	216	222	229	236	244	252	261	270	280
75	75	77	79	82	84	87	90	93	96	100	215	215	221	228	235	242	250	258	267	276	287
80	80	82	85	87	90	93	96	99	103	107	220	220	226	233	240	247	255	264	273	283	293
85	85	87	90	93	96	99	102	106	109	113	225	225	231	238	245	253	261	270	279	289	300
90	90	93	95	98	101	105	108	112	116	120	230	230	237	244	251	259	267	276	286	296	307
95	95	98	101	104	107	110	114	118	122	127	235	235	242	249	256	264	273	282	292	302	313
100	100	103	106	109	112	116	120	124	129	133	240	240	247	254	262	270	279	288	298	309	320
105	105	108	111	115	118	122	126	130	135	140	245	245	252	259	267	276	285	294	304	315	327
110	110	113	116	120	124	128	132	137	141	147	250	250	257	265	273	281	290	300	310	321	333
115	115	118	122	125	129	134	138	143	148	153	255	256	262	270	278	287	296	306	317	328	340
120	120	123	127	131	135	139	144	149	154	160	260	260	267	275	284	292	302	312	323	334	347
125	125	129	132	136	141	145	150	155	161	167	265	265	273	281	289	298	308	318	329	341	353
130	130	134	138	142	146	151	156	161	167	173	270	270	278	286	295	304	314	324	335	347	360
135	135	139	143	147	152	157	162	168	174	180	275	275	283	291	300	309	319	330	341	354	367
140	140	144	148	153	157	163	168	174	180	187	280	280	288	296	305	315	325	336	348	360	373
145	145	149	154	158	163	168	174	180	186	193	285	285	293	302	311	321	331	342	354	366	380
150	150	154	159	164	169	174	180	186	193	200	290	290	298	307	316	326	337	348	360	373	387
155	155	159	164	169	174	180	186	192	199	207	295	295	303	312	322	332	343	354	366	379	393
160	160	165	169	175	180	186	192	199	206	213	300	300	309	318	327	337	348	360	372	386	400
165	165	170	175	180	186	192	198	205	212	220	305	305	314	323	333	343	354	366	379	392	407

Source: JOPERD.

Chart 2 Fitness Classification for Relative Strength in Men and Women (1RM/Body Weight)

Age:	Leg Press			Arm Press		
	30 or Less	31–50	51+	30 or Less	31–50	51+
Ratings for Men						
High-performance zone	2.06+	1.81+	1.61+	1.26+	1.01+	.86+
Good fitness zone	1.96–2.05	1.66–1.80	1.51–1.60	1.11–1.25	.91–1.00	.76–.85
Marginal zone	1.76–1.95	1.51–1.65	1.41–1.50	.96–1.10	.86–.90	.66–.75
Low fitness zone	1.75 or less	1.50 or less	1.40 or less	.95 or less	.85 or less	.65 or less
Ratings for Women						
High-performance zone	1.61+	1.36+	1.16+	.76+	.61+	.51+
Good fitness zone	1.46–1.60	1.21–1.35	1.06–1.15	.66–.75	.56–.60	.46–.50
Marginal zone	1.31–1.45	1.11–1.20	.96–1.05	.56–.65	.51–.55	.41–.45
Low fitness zone	1.30 or less	1.10 or less	.95 or less	.55 or less	.50 or less	.40 or less

Evaluating Muscular Endurance

1. Curl-Up (Dynamic)

Sit on a mat or carpet with your legs bent more than 90 degrees so your feet remain flat on the floor (about halfway between 90 degrees and straight). Make two tape marks 4½ inches apart or lay a 4½-inch strip of paper or cardboard on the floor. Lie with your arms extended at your sides, palms down and the fingers extended so that your fingertips touch one tape mark (or one side of the paper or cardboard strip). Keeping your heels in contact with the floor, curl the head and shoulders forward until your fingers reach 4½ inches (second piece of tape or other side of strip). Lower slowly to beginning position. Repeat one curl-up every 3 seconds. Continue until you are unable to keep the pace of one curl-up every 3 seconds.

Two partners may be helpful. One stands on the cardboard strip (to prevent movement) if one is used. The second assures that the head returns to the floor after each repetition.

Evaluating Isometric Strength

Test: Grip Strength

Adjust a hand dynamometer to fit your hand size. Squeeze it as hard as possible. You may bend or straighten the arm, but do not touch the body with your hand, elbow, or arm. Perform with both right and left hands. *Note:* When not being tested, perform the basic eight isometric strength exercises, or squeeze and indent a new tennis ball (*after* completing the dynamometer test).

2. Ninety-Degree Push-Up (Dynamic)

Support the body in a push-up position from the toes. The hands should be just outside the shoulders, the back and legs straight, and toes tucked under. Lower the body until the upper arm is parallel to the floor or the elbow is bent at 90 degrees. The rhythm should be approximately 1 push-up every 3 seconds. Repeat as many times as possible up to 35.

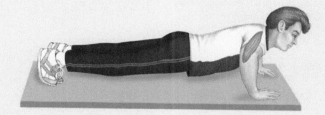

3. Flexed-Arm Support (Static)

Women: Support the body in a push-up position from the knees. The hands should be outside the shoulders, the back and legs straight. Lower the body until the upper arm is parallel to the floor or the elbow is flexed at 90 degrees.

Men: Use the same procedure as for women except support the push-up position from the toes instead of the knees. (Same position as for 90-degree push-up.) Hold the 90-degree position as long as possible, up to 35 seconds.

Chart 3 Isometric Strength Rating Scale (Pounds)

Classification	Left Grip	Right Grip	Total Score
Ratings for Men			
High-performance zone	125+	135+	260+
Good fitness zone	100–124	110–134	210–259
Marginal zone	90–99	95–109	185–209
Low fitness zone	<90	<95	<185
Ratings for Women			
High-performance zone	75+	85+	160+
Good fitness zone	60–74	70–84	130–159
Marginal zone	45–59	50–69	95–129
Low fitness zone	<45	<50	<95

Suitable for use by young adults between 18 and 30 years of age. After 30, an adjustment of 0.5 of 1 percent per year is appropriate because some loss of muscle tissue typically occurs as you grow older.

Chart 4 Rating Scale for Dynamic Muscular Endurance

Age:	17–26		27–39		40–49		50–59		60+	
Classification	Curl-Ups	Push-Ups	Curl-Ups	Push-Ups	Curl-Ups	Push-Ups	Curl-Ups	Push-Ups	Curl-Ups	Push-Ups
Ratings for Men										
High-performance zone	35+	29+	34+	27+	33+	26+	32+	24+	31+	22+
Good fitness zone	24–34	20–28	23–33	18–26	22–32	17–25	21–31	15–23	20–30	13–21
Marginal zone	15–23	16–19	14–22	15–17	13–21	14–16	12–20	12–14	11–19	10–12
Low fitness zone	<15	<16	<14	<15	<13	<14	<12	<12	<11	<10
Ratings for Women										
High-performance zone	25+	17+	24+	16+	23+	15+	22+	14+	21+	13+
Good fitness zone	18–24	12–16	17–23	11–15	16–22	10–14	15–21	9–13	14–20	8–12
Marginal zone	10–17	8–11	9–16	7–10	8–15	6–9	7–14	5–8	6–13	4–7
Low fitness zone	<10	<8	<9	<7	<8	<6	<7	<5	<6	<4

Chart 5 Rating Scale for Static Endurance (Flexed-Arm Support)

Classification	Score in Seconds
High-performance zone	30+
Good fitness zone	20–29
Marginal zone	10–19
Low fitness zone	<10

Lab 9A Evaluating Muscle Strength: 1RM and Grip Strength

Name	Section	Date

Purpose: To evaluate your muscle strength using 1RM and to determine the best amount of resistance to use for various strength exercises

Procedures: 1RM is the maximum amount of resistance you can lift for a specific exercise. Testing yourself to determine how much you can lift only one time using traditional methods can be fatiguing and even dangerous. The procedure you will perform here allows you to estimate 1RM based on the number of times you can lift a weight that is less than 1RM.

Evaluating Strength Using Estimated 1RM

1. Use a resistance machine for the leg press and arm or bench press for the evaluation part of this lab.
2. Estimate how much weight you can lift two or three times. Be conservative; it is better to start with too little weight than too much. If you lift a weight more than 10 times, the procedure should be done again on another day when you are rested.
3. Using correct form, perform a leg press with the weight you have chosen. Perform as many times as you can up to 10.
4. Use Chart 1 in *Lab Resource Materials* to determine your 1RM for the leg press. Find the weight used in the left-hand column and then find the number of repetitions you performed across the top of the chart.
5. Your 1RM score is the value where the weight row and the repetitions column intersect.
6. Repeat this procedure for the arm or bench press using the same technique.
7. Record your 1RM scores for the leg press and bench press in the Results section.
8. Next divide your 1RM scores by your body weight in pounds to get a "strength per pound of body weight" (1RM/ body weight) score for each of the two exercises.
9. Determine your strength rating for your upper body strength (arm press) and lower body (leg press) using Chart 2 in *Lab Resource Materials.* Record in the Results section. If time allows, assess 1RM for other exercises you choose to perform (see Lab 9C).
10. If a grip dynamometer is available, determine your right-hand and left-hand grip strength using the procedures in *Lab Resource Materials*. Use Chart 3 in *Lab Resource Materials* to rate your grip (isometric) strength.

Results

Arm press: Wt. selected [   ] Reps [   ] Estimated 1RM [   ]
(or bench press) (Chart 1, *Lab Resource Materials,* page 187)

Strength per lb. body weight [   ] Rating [   ]
(1RM ÷ body weight) (Chart 2, *Lab Resource Materials,* page 188)

Leg press: Wt. selected [   ] Reps [   ] Estimated 1RM [   ]
(Chart 1, *Lab Resource Materials,* page 187)

Strength per lb. body weight [   ] Rating [   ]
(1RM ÷ body weight) (Chart 2, *Lab Resource Materials,* page 188)

Grip strength: Right grip score [   ] Right grip rating [   ]

Left grip score [   ] Left grip rating [   ]

Total score [   ] Total rating [   ]

(Chart 3, *Lab Resource Materials,* page 190)

Seated Press (Arm Press)

This test can be performed using a seated press (see below) or using a bench press machine. When using the seated press, position the seat height so that arm handles are directly in front of the chest. Position backrest so that hands are at comfortable distance away from the chest. Push handles forward to full extension and return to starting position in a slow and controlled manner. Repeat. Note: Machine may have a foot lever to help position, raise, and lower the weight.

Leg Press

To perform this test, use a leg press machine. Typically, the beginning position is with the knees bent at right angles with the feet placed on the press machine pedals or a foot platform. Extend the legs and return to beginning position. Do not lock the knees when the legs are straightened. Typically, handles are provided. Grasp the handles with the hands when performing this test.

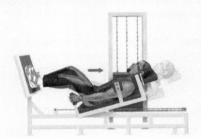

Conclusions and Implications: In several sentences, discuss your current strength, whether you believe it is adequate for good health, and whether you think that your "strength per pound of body weight" scores are representative of your true strength.

Lab 9B Evaluating Muscular Endurance

Name	**Section**	**Date**

Purpose: To evaluate the dynamic muscular endurance of two muscle groups and the static endurance of the arms and trunk muscles

Procedures

1. Perform the curl-up, push-up, and flexed-arm support tests described in *Lab Resource Materials* (pp. 188–189).
2. Record your test scores in the Results section. Determine and record your rating in Chart 1 below, based on Charts 4 and 5 in *Lab Resource Materials* (page 190).

1. Curl-up (dynamic)

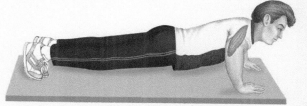

2. Ninety-degree push-up (dynamic)

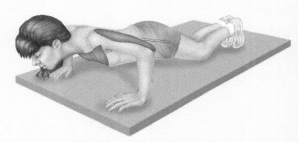

3. Flexed-arm support (static): women in knee position and men in full support position

Results

Record your scores below.

Curl-up [ ]   Push-up [ ]   Flexed-arm support (seconds) [ ]

Check your ratings in Chart 1.

Chart 1 Rating Scale

	Curl-Up	Push-Up	Flexed-Arm Support
High	○	○	○
Good	○	○	○
Marginal	○	○	○
Poor	○	○	○

On which of the tests of muscular endurance did you score the lowest?

Curl-up ◯　Push-up ◯　Flexed-arm support ◯

On which of the tests of muscular endurance did you score the best?

Curl-up ◯　Push-up ◯　Flexed-arm support ◯

Conclusions and Implications: In several sentences, discuss your current level of muscular endurance and whether this level is enough to meet your health, work, and leisure-time needs in the future.

Lab 9C Planning and Logging Muscle Fitness Exercises: Free Weights or Resistance Machines

Name	**Section**	**Date**

Purpose: To set lifestyle goals for muscle fitness exercise, to prepare a muscle fitness exercise plan, and to self-monitor progress for the 1-week plan

Procedures

1. Using Chart 1, provide some background information about your experience with resistance exercise, your goals, and your plans for incorporating these exercises into your normal exercise routine.
2. Using Chart 2, select at least eight muscle fitness exercises by circling the name of the exercises or writing in the name of the exercises. Perform the exercises for 2 or 3 days. Record the weight, reps, and sets performed on each day. Be sure that you plan your exercise program so it fits with the goals you described in Chart 1. If you are just starting out, it is best to start with light weights and more repetitions, e.g., 12–15. For best results, take the log with you during your workout, so you can remember the weights, reps, and sets you performed.
3. Describe your experiences with your resistance exercise program. Be sure to comment on your plans for future resistance exercise.

Chart 1 Muscle Fitness Survey

1. Determine your current stage for resistance exercise. Check only the stage that represents your current activity level.

   ◯ Precontemplation. I do not meet resistance exercise guidelines and have not been thinking about starting.

   ◯ Contemplation. I do not do resistance exercises but have been thinking about starting.

   ◯ Preparation. I am planning to start doing regular resistance exercises to meet guidelines.

   ◯ Action. I do resistance exercises, but I am not as regular as I should be.

   ◯ Maintenance. I regularly meet guidelines for resistance exercises.

2. What are your primary goals for resistance exercise?

   ◯ General conditioning   ◯ Improved appearance   ◯ Other_____

   ◯ Sports training   ◯ Avoidance of back pain

3. Are you currently involved in a regular resistance exercise program?

   ◯ Yes   ◯ No

4. Describe your current program or your future goals.

   - What days and times do you lift weights (or when can you lift)?
   - Where do you lift (or where can you lift)?
   - Describe your goals (or plans) for resistance exercise:

Chart 2   Muscle Fitness Exercise Log

Check the exercises you performed and the days you performed them. You can do all free weights, all machines, or some of both. List others that you added.

Exercises	Day 1 (date)			Day 2 (date)			Day 3 (date)		
	Wt.	Reps	Sets	Wt.	Reps	Sets	Wt.	Reps	Sets
Free Weight Exercises									
1 Bench press									
2 Overhead press									
3 Biceps curl									
4 Triceps curl									
5 Wrist curl									
6 Dumbbell rowing									
7 Half squat									
8 Lunge									
9									
10									
Machine Exercises									
11 Chest press									
12 Overhead press									
13 Biceps curl									
14 Triceps press									
15 Lat pull-down									
16 Seated rowing									
17 Knee extension									
18 Hamstring curl									
19									
20									

Results

Were you able to do your basic eight exercises at least 2 days in the week?   Yes ◯   No ◯

Conclusions and Implications: Do you feel that you will use muscle fitness exercises as part of your regular lifetime physical activity plan, either now or in the future? Comment on what modifications you would make in your program in the future. Use several sentences to answer.

Lab 9D Planning and Logging Muscle Fitness Exercises: Calisthenics or Core Exercises

Name	**Section**	**Date**

Purpose: To set lifestyle goals for muscle fitness exercises that can easily be performed at home, to prepare a muscle fitness exercise plan, and to self-monitor progress for a 1-week plan

Procedures

1. Using Chart 1, provide some background information about your experience with calisthenic or core exercise, your goals, and your plans for incorporating these exercises into your normal exercise routine.
2. Using Chart 2, select at least eight calisthenics or core exercises by circling the name of the exercises or writing in the name of the exercises. Perform the exercises for 2 or 3 days. Record the reps and sets performed on each day.
3. Describe your experiences with your resistance exercise program. Be sure to comment on your plans for future resistance exercise.

Chart 1 Muscle Fitness Survey

1. Determine your current stage for calisthenics or core exercise. Check only the stage that represents your current activity level.

○ Precontemplation. I do not do calisthenics or core exercises and have not been thinking about starting.

○ Contemplation. I do not do calisthenics or core exercises but have been thinking about starting.

○ Preparation. I am planning to start doing calisthenics or core exercises.

○ Action. I do calisthenics or core exercises, but I am not as regular as I should be.

○ Maintenance. I regularly perform calisthenics or core exercises.

2. What is your level of experience with core exercises (refer to Table 10 on pages 185 and 186)? Check the box that best describes you.

○ I have done abdominal exercises but have never done the other core exercises.

○ I have done abdominal exercises and have tried core exercises with the Bosu® or similar devices.

○ I regularly perform core exercises and am very experienced with the Bosu® or similar devices.

3. What are your primary reasons for doing calisthenic or core exercise?

○ General conditioning

○ Sports training

○ Improved appearance

○ Avoidance of back pain

4. Describe your current program or your present or future goals.
   - What days and times do you exercise (or when can you exercise)?
   - Where do you perform these exercises (or where can you exercise)?
   - Describe your goals/plans:

Lab 9D

Planning and Logging Muscle Fitness Exercises

Chart 2 Muscle Fitness Exercise Log

Check the exercises you performed and the days you performed them. List others that you added.

Exercises	Day 1 (date)		Day 2 (date)		Day 3 (date)	
	Reps	Sets	Reps	Sets	Reps	Sets
Calisthenic Exercises						
1 Bent knee push-ups						
2 Modified pull-ups						
3 Dips						
4 Crunch (curl-up)						
5 Trunk lift						
6 Side leg raise						
7 Lower leg lift						
8 Alternate leg kneel						
9						
10						
Core Exercises						
11 Crunch						
12 Reverse curl						
13 Crunch with twist						
14 Sitting tucks						
15 Hands and knees balance						
16 Marching						
17 Side step						
18 Squatting						
19						
20						

Results

Were you able to do your planned exercises at least 2 days in the week?   Yes ◯   No ◯

Conclusions and Implications: Do you feel that you will use these muscle fitness exercises as part of your regular lifetime physical activity plan, either now or in the future? Discuss the exercises you feel benefited you and the ones that did not. What modifications would you make in your program for it to work better for you?

Lab Resource Materials: Flexibility Tests

Directions: To test the flexibility of all joints is impractical. These tests are for joints used frequently. Follow the instructions carefully. Determine your flexibility using Chart 1.

Test

1. *Modified Sit-and-Reach* (Flexibility Test of Hamstrings)

   a. Remove shoes and sit on the floor. Place the sole of the foot of the extended leg flat against a box or bench. Bend opposite knee and place the head, back, and hips against a wall with a 90-degree angle at the hips.

   b. Place one hand over the other and slowly reach forward as far as you can with arms fully extended. Keep head and back in contact with the wall. A partner will slide the measuring stick on the bench until it touches the fingertips.

   c. With the measuring stick fixed in the new position, reach forward as far as possible, three times, holding the position on the third reach for at least 2 seconds while the partner records the distance on the ruler. Keep the knee of the extended leg straight (see illustration).

   d. Repeat the test a second time and average the scores of the two trials.

Test

2. *Shoulder Flexibility* ("Zipper" Test)

   a. Raise your arm, bend your elbow, and reach down across your back as far as possible.

   b. At the same time, extend your left arm down and behind your back, bend your elbow up across your back, and try to cross your fingers over those of your right hand as shown in the accompanying illustration.

   c. Measure the distance to the nearest half-inch. If your fingers overlap, score as a plus. If they fail to meet, score as a minus; use a zero if your fingertips just touch.

   d. Repeat with your arms crossed in the opposite direction (left arm up). Most people will find that they are more flexible on one side than the other.

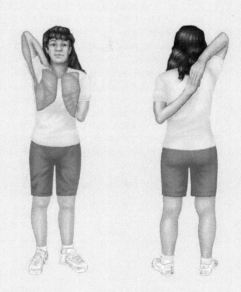

Test

3. *Hamstring and Hip Flexor Flexibility*

a. Lie on your back on the floor beside a wall.

b. Slowly lift one leg off the floor. Keep the other leg flat on the floor.

c. Keep both legs straight.

d. Continue to lift the leg until either leg begins to bend or the lower leg begins to lift off the floor.

e. Place a yardstick against the wall and underneath the lifted leg.

f. Hold the yardstick against the wall after the leg is lowered.

g. Using a protractor, measure the angle created by the floor and the yardstick. The greater the angle, the better your score.

h. Repeat with the other leg.*

*Note: For ease of testing, you may want to draw angles on a piece of posterboard, as illustrated. If you have goniometers, you may be taught to use them instead.

Test

4. *Trunk Rotation*

a. Tape two yardsticks to the wall at shoulder height, one right side up and the other upside down.

b. Stand with your left shoulder an arm's length (fist closed) from the wall. Toes should be on the line, which is perpendicular to the wall and even with the 15-inch mark on the yardstick.

c. Drop the left arm and raise the right arm to the side, palm down, fist closed.

d. Without moving your feet, rotate the trunk to the right as far as possible, reaching along the yardstick, and hold it 2 seconds. Do not move the feet or bend the trunk. Your knees may bend slightly.

e. A partner will read the distance reached to the nearest half-inch. Record your score. Repeat two times and average your two scores.

f. Next, perform the test facing the opposite direction. Rotate to the left. For this test, you will use the second yardstick (upside down) so that, the greater the rotation, the higher the score. If you have only one yardstick, turn it right side up for the first test and upside down for the second test.

15-inch mark

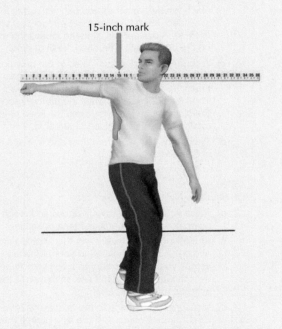

Chart 1 Flexibility Rating Scale for Tests 1–4

Classification	Men					Women				
	Test 1	Test 2		Test 3	Test 4	Test 1	Test 2		Test 3	Test 4
		Right Up	Left Up				Right Up	Left Up		
High performance*	16+	5+	4+	111+	20+	17+	6+	5+	111+	20.5 or >
Good fitness zone	13–15	1–4	1–3	80–110	16–19.5	14–16	2–5	2–4	80–110	17–20
Marginal zone	10–12	0	0	60–79	13.5–15.5	11–13	1	1	60–79	14.5–16.5
Low zone	<9	<0	<0	<60	<13.5	<10	<1	<1	<60	<14.5

*Though performers need good flexibility, hypermobility may increase injury risk.

Lab 10A Evaluating Flexibility

Name	Section	Date

Purpose: To evaluate your flexibility in several joints

Procedures

1. Take the flexibility tests outlined in *Lab Resource Materials,* pages 219–220.
2. Record your scores in the Results section.
3. Use Chart 1 in *Lab Resource Materials* (page 218) to determine your ratings on the self-assessments; then place an X over the circle for the appropriate rating.

Results

Flexibility Scores and Ratings

Record Scores			High Performance	Good Fitness	Marginal	Low
Modified sit-and-reach						
Test 1	Left		○	○	○	○
	Right		○	○	○	○
Zipper						
Test 2	Left		○	○	○	○
	Right		○	○	○	○
Hamstring/hip flexor						
Test 3	Left		○	○	○	○
	Right		○	○	○	○
Trunk rotation						
Test 4	Left		○	○	○	○
	Right		○	○	○	○

Record Ratings

Lab 10A

Evaluating Flexibility

Do any of these muscle groups need stretching? Check yes or no for each muscle group.

	Yes	No
Back of the thighs and knees (hamstrings)	◯	◯
Calf muscles	◯	◯
Lower back (lumbar region)	◯	◯
Front of right shoulder	◯	◯
Back of right shoulder	◯	◯
Front of left shoulder	◯	◯
Back of left shoulder	◯	◯
Most of the body	◯	◯
Trunk muscles	◯	◯

Conclusions and Implications: In several sentences, discuss your current flexibility and your flexibility needs for the future. Include comments about your current state of flexibility, need for improvement in specific areas, and special flexibility needs for sports or other special activities.

Lab 10B Planning and Logging Stretching Exercises

Name	Section	Date

Purpose: To set 1-week lifestyle goals for stretching exercises, to prepare a stretching for flexibility plan, and to self-monitor progress in your 1-week plan

Procedures

1. Using Chart 1, provide some background information about your experience with stretching exercise, your goals, and your plans for incorporating these exercises into your normal exercise routine.
2. In Chart 2, keep a log of your actual participation in stretching exercise. You can choose from any of the stretching exercises described in Table 3, 4, or 5. Try to pick at least eight exercises and perform them at least 3 days in the week (ideally every day).
3. Describe your experiences with your stretching exercise program. Be sure to comment on your plans for future stretching exercise.

Chart 1 Stretching Exercise Survey

1. Determine your current stage for flexibility exercise. Check only the stage that represents your current activity level.

   ◯ Precontemplation. I do not meet flexibility exercise guidelines and have not been thinking about starting.

   ◯ Contemplation. I do not meet flexibility exercise guidelines but have been thinking about starting.

   ◯ Preparation. I am planning to start doing regular flexibility exercises to meet guidelines.

   ◯ Action. I do flexibility exercises, but I am not as regular as I should be.

   ◯ Maintenance. I regularly meet guidelines for flexibility exercises.

2. What are your primary goals for flexibility exercise?

   ◯ General conditioning

   ◯ Sports improvement (specify sport:_____)

   ◯ Health benefits

3. Are you currently involved in a regular stretching program? If yes, describe your program. If no, describe barriers that have prevented you from stretching.

   ◯ Yes

   ◯ No

Results

	Yes	No
Did you do eight exercises at least 3 days in the week?	◯	◯
Did you do eight exercises more than 3 days in the week?	◯	◯

Chart 2 Stretching Exercise Log

List the stretching exercises you actually performed and the days on which you performed them.	Day 1 Date:	Day 2 Date:	Day 3 Date:	Day 4 Date:	Day 5 Date:	Day 6 Date:	Day 7 Date:
1.							
2.							
3.							
4.							
5.							
6.							
7.							
8.							

Conclusions and Interpretations

1. Do you feel that you will use stretching exercises as part of your regular lifetime physical activity plan, either now or in the future? Use several sentences to explain your answer.

2. Discuss the exercises you feel benefited you and the ones that did not. What exercises would you continue to do and which ones would you change? Use several sentences to explain your answer.

Physical Activity: Special Considerations

Lab Resource Materials: Healthy Back Tests

Chart 1 Healthy Back Tests

Physicians and therapists use these tests, among others, to make differential diagnoses of back problems. You and your partner can use them to determine if you have muscle tightness that may put you at risk for back problems. Discontinue any of these tests if they produce pain, numbness, or tingling sensations in the back, hips, or legs. Experiencing any of these sensations may be an indication that you have a low back problem that requires diagnosis by your physician. Partners should use *great caution* in applying force. Be gentle and listen to your partner's feedback.

FLEXIBILITY

Test 1—Straight-Leg Lift

Lie on your back with hands behind your neck. The partner on your left should stabilize your right leg by placing his or her right hand on your knee. With the left hand, your partner should grasp your left ankle and raise your left leg as near to a right angle as possible. In this position (as shown in the diagram), your lower back should be in contact with the floor. Your right leg should remain straight and on the floor throughout the test.

If your left leg bends at the knee, this indicates short hamstring muscles. If your back arches and/or your right leg does not remain flat on the floor this indicates short lumbar muscles or hip flexor muscles. To pass the test, each leg should be able to reach approximately 90 degress without the knee or back bending. (Both sides must pass in order to pass the test.)

Test 2—Thomas Test

Lie on your back on a table or bench with your right leg extended beyond the edge of the table (approximately one-third of your thigh off the table). Bring your left knee to your chest and pull your thigh down tightly with your hands. Lower your right leg. Your lower back should remain flat against the table, as shown in the diagram. To pass the test, your right thigh should be at table level or lower.

Test 3—Ober Test

Lie on your left side with your left leg flexed 90 degrees at the hip and 90 degrees at the knee. A partner should place your right hip in slight extension and right knee with just a slight bend (~20 degrees flexion). Your partner stabilizes your pelvis with the left hand to prevent movement. Your partner then allows the weight of the top leg to lower the leg to the floor. To pass the test your knee or upper leg should be able to touch the table.

CORE TRUNK ENDURANCE TESTS

Test 4—Leg Drop Test*

Lie on your back on a table or on the floor with both legs extended overhead. Flatten your low back against the table or floor by tightening your abdominals. Slowly lower your legs while keeping your back flat.

If your back arches before you reach a 45-degree angle, your abdominal muscles are too weak and you fail the test. A partner should be ready to support your legs if needed to prevent your lower back from arching or strain to the back muscles.

*The Leg Drop Test is suitable as a diagnostic test when performed one time. It is not a good exercise to be performed regularly by most people. If it causes pain, stop the test.

Chart 1 Healthy Back Tests *(Continued)*

Test 5—Isometric Abdominal Test. Lie supine with hips bent 45 degrees, feet flat on the floor and arms by the side. Draw a line 4 1/2 inches beyond fingertips. Tuck chin and curl trunk forward, touching line with fingers. To pass, hold for 30 seconds.

Test 6—Isometric Extensor Test. Lie on a table with upper half of the body hanging over the edge and arms crossed in front of chest. Have a partner stabilize your feet and legs. Raise your trunk smoothly until your back is in a horizontal position parallel to the floor. Do not arch the back. To pass the test hold this position for 30 seconds.

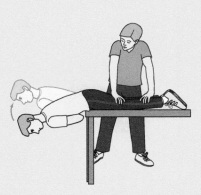

Test 7—Prone Bridge. Support yourself on the floor by resting on forearms and balls of feet, body extended and back straight. Elbows are placed directly underneath shoulders. Look straight down toward hands. Do not arch the back. To pass the test hold this position for 30 seconds.

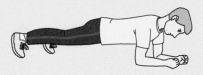

Test 8—Quadruped Stabilization. Begin on hands and knees. Place hands directly below shoulders and knees directly below hips. Draw abdominals in. Extend one arm and opposite leg to a horizontal position. Do not allow back to arch or body to sway. To pass, hold position for 30 seconds.

Test 9—Right Lateral Bridge. Lie on your right side with legs extended. Raise pelvis off the floor until trunk is straight and body weight is supported on arm and feet. Do not roll forward or backward. Do not arch back. Hold this position for 30 seconds.

Test 10—Left Lateral Bridge. Lie on your left side with legs extended. Raise pelvis off the floor until trunk is straight and body weight is supported on arm and feet. Do not roll forward or backward or arch back. To pass the test, hold this position for 30 seconds.

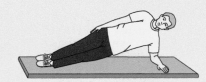

Chart 2 Healthy Back Test Ratings

Classification	Number of Tests Passed
Excellent	8–10
Very good	7
Good	6
Fair	5
Poor	1–4

Lab 11A The Healthy Back Tests and Back/Neck Questionnaire

Name	Section	Date

Purpose: To self-assess your potential for back problems using the Healthy Back Tests and the back/neck questionnaire

Procedures

1. Answer the questions in the following back/neck questionnaire. Count your points for nonmodifiable factors, modifiable factors, and total score, and record these scores in the Results section. Use Chart 1 to determine your rating for all three scores and record them in the Results section.
2. With a partner, administer the Healthy Back Tests to each other (see *Lab Resource Materials*). Determine your rating using Chart 2. Record your score and rating in the Results section. If you did not pass a test, list the muscles you should develop to improve on that test.
3. Complete the Conclusions and Implications section.

Risk-Factor Questionnaire for Back and Neck Problems

Directions: Place an X in the appropriate circle after each question. Add the scores for each of the circles you checked to determine your modifiable risk, nonmodifiable risk, and total risk scores.

Nonmodifiable

1. Do you have a family history of osteoporosis, arthritis, rheumatism, or other joint disease?
   - (0) No (1) Yes

2. What is your age?
   - (0) <40 (1) 40–50 (2) 51–60 (3) 61+

3. Did you participate extensively in these sports when you were young: gymnastics, football, weight lifting, skiing, ballet, javelin, or shot put?
   - (0) No (1) Some (3) Extensive

4. How many previous back or neck problems have you had?
   - (0) None (1) 1 (2) 2 (5) 3+

Modifiable

5. Does your daily routine involve heavy lifting?
   - (0) No (1) Some (3) A lot

6. Does your daily routine require you to stand for long periods?
   - (0) No (1) Some (3) A lot

7. Do you have a high level of job-related stress?
   - (0) No (1) Some (3) A lot

8. Do you sit for long periods of time (computer operator, typist, or similar job)?
   - (0) No (1) Some (3) A lot

9. Does your daily routine require doing repetitive movements or holding objects (e.g., baby, briefcase, sales suitcase) for long periods of time?
   - (0) No (1) Some (3) A lot

10. Does your daily routine require you to stand or sit with poor posture (e.g., sitting in a low car seat, reaching overhead with head tilted back)?
    - (0) No (1) Some (3) A lot

11. What is your score on the Healthy Back Tests?
    - (0) 6–7 (1) 5 (3) 4 (5) 0–3

12. What is your score on the posture test in Lab 11B?
    - (0) 0–2 (1) 3–4 (3) 5–7 (5) 8+

Lab 11A

The Healthy Back Tests and Back/Neck Questionnaire

Results

Tests	Pass	Fail	If you failed, what exercise should you do?
1. Straight-leg lift	○	○	
2. Thomas test	○	○	
3. Ober test	○	○	
4. Leg drop test	○	○	
5. Isometric abdominal test	○	○	
6. Isometric extensor test	○	○	
7. Prone bridge	○	○	
8. Quadruped stabilization	○	○	
9. Right lateral bridge	○	○	
10. Left lateral bridge	○	○	

Total ☐

Chart 1 Back/Neck Questionnaire Ratings

Rating	Modifiable Score	Nonmodifiable Score	Total Score
Very high risk	7+	12+	19+
High risk	5–6	8–11	13–17
Average risk	3–4	4–7	7–11
Low risk	0–2	0–3	0–5

Chart 2 Healthy Back Tests Ratings

Classification	Number of Tests Passed
Excellent	8–10
Very good	7
Good	6
Fair	5
Poor	1–4

Back/Neck Questionnaire

Score ☐   Rating ☐

Back Tests

Score ☐   Rating ☐

Conclusions and Implications: In several sentences, discuss your need to do exercises for care of the back and neck. Include in your discussion whether you think your muscles are fit enough to prevent problems, the areas in which you are most likely to experience problems, and steps you might take to prevent future problems. Use your test results to answer.

Lab 11B Evaluating Posture

Name	**Section**	**Date**

Purpose: To learn to recognize postural deviations and thus become more posture conscious and to determine your postural limitations in order to institute a preventive or corrective program

Procedures

1. Wear as little clothing as possible (bathing suits are recommended) and remove shoes and socks.
2. Work in groups of two or three, with one person acting as the subject while partners serve as examiners; then alternate roles.
   a. Stand by a vertical plumb line.
   b. Using Chart 1 and Figure 1, check any deviations and indicate their severity using the following point scale (0 = none, 1 = slight, 2 = moderate, and 3 = severe).
   c. Total the score and determine your posture rating from the Posture Rating Scale (Chart 2).
3. If time permits, perform back and posture exercises (see Lab 11C).
4. Complete the Conclusions and Implications section.

Results

Record your posture score:

Record your posture rating from the Posture Rating Scale in Chart 2:

Chart 1 Posture Evaluation

Side View	Points
Forward head	
Rounded shoulders	
Excessive lordosis (lumbar)	
Abdominal ptosis	
Hyperextended knees	
Total scores	

Chart 2 Posture Rating Scale

Classification	Total Score
Excellent	0–3
Very good	4–6
Good	7–9
Fair	10–12
Poor	12 or more

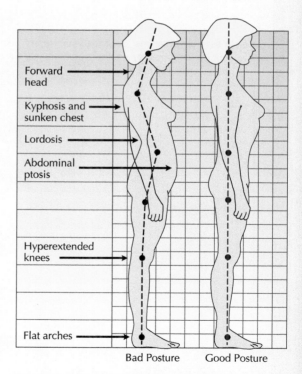

Forward head

Kyphosis and sunken chest

Lordosis

Abdominal ptosis

Hyperextended knees

Flat arches

Bad Posture   Good Posture

Figure 1 ▶ Comparison of bad and good posture.

Lab 11B Evaluating Posture

Conclusions and Implications

Were you aware of the deviations that were found?   Yes ◯   No ◯

1. List the deviations that were moderate or severe (use several complete sentences).

2. In several sentences, describe your current posture status. Include in this discussion your overall assessment of your current posture, whether you think you will need special exercises in the future, and the reasons your posture rating is good or not so good.

Lab 11C Planning and Logging Exercises: Care of the Back and Neck

Name		Section	Date

Purpose: To select several exercises for the back and neck that meet your personal needs and to self-monitor progress for one of these

Procedures

1. On Chart 1, check the tests from the Healthy Back Tests that you did *not* pass. Select at least one exercise from the group associated with those items. In addition, select several more exercises (a total of 8 to 10) that you think will best meet your personal needs. If you passed all of the items, select 8 to 10 exercises that you think will best prevent future back and neck problems. Check the exercises you plan to perform in Chart 1.
2. Perform each of the exercises you select 3 days in 1 week.
3. Keep a 1-week log of your actual participation using the last three columns in Chart 1. If possible, keep the log with you during the day. Place a check by each of the exercises you perform for each day, including ones that you didn't originally plan. If you cannot keep the log with you, fill in the log at the end of the day. If you choose to keep a log for more than 1 week, make extra copies of the log before you begin.
4. Answer the question in the Results section.

Chart 1 Back and Neck Exercise Plan					
Check the tests you failed.	**✓**	**Write in a selected exercise for each test that you can plan to perform this week. [The core tests (5–10) may be used as strengthening exercises]. Check the dates you performed the exercises.**	**Day 1** Date:	**Day 2** Date:	**Day 3** Date:
1. Straight-leg lift					
2. Thomas test					
3. Ober test					
4. Leg drop test					
5. Isometric abdominal test					
6. Isometric extensor test					
7. Prone bridge					
8. Quadruped stabilization					
9. Right lateral bridge					
10. Left lateral bridge					

Lab 11C

Planning and Logging Exercises: Care of the Back and Neck

Results

Did you do 8 to 10 exercises at least 3 days in the week?   Yes ◯   No ◯

Conclusions and Interpretations

1. Do you feel that you will use back and neck exercises as part of your regular lifetime physical activity plan, either now or in the future? Use several sentences to explain your answer.

2. Discuss the exercises you did. What exercises would you continue to do, and which ones would you change? Use several sentences to explain your answer.

Lab Resource Materials: Skill-Related Physical Fitness

Important Note: Because skill-related physical fitness does not relate to good health, the rating charts used in this section differ from those used for health-related fitness. The rating charts that follow can be used to compare your scores with those of other people. You *do not* need exceptional scores on skill-related fitness to be able to enjoy sports and other types of physical activity; however, it is necessary for high-level performance. After the age of 30, you should adjust ratings by 1 percent per year.

Evaluating Skill-Related Physical Fitness

I. Evaluating Agility: The Illinois Agility Run

An agility course using four chairs 10 feet apart and a 30-foot running area will be set up as depicted in this illustration. The test is performed as follows:

1. Lie prone with your hands by your shoulders and your head at the starting line. On the signal to begin, get on your feet and run the course as fast as possible.
2. Your score is the time required to complete the course.

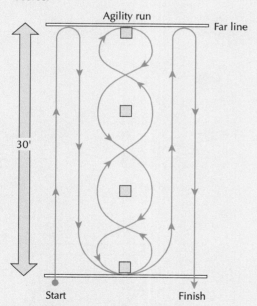

II. Evaluating Balance: The Bass Test of Dynamic Balance

Eleven circles (9½ inches) are drawn on the floor as shown in the illustration. The test is performed as follows:

1. Stand on the right foot in circle X. *Leap* forward to circle 1, then circle 2 through 10, alternating feet with each leap.
2. The feet must leave the floor on each leap and the heel may not touch. Only the ball of the foot and toes may land on the floor.
3. Remain in each circle for 5 seconds before leaping to the next circle. (A count of 5 will be made for you aloud.)
4. Practice trials are allowed.
5. The score is 50, plus the number of seconds taken to complete the test, minus the number of errors.
6. For every error, deduct 3 points each. Errors include touching the heel, moving the supporting foot, touching outside a circle, and touching any body part other than the supporting foot to the floor.

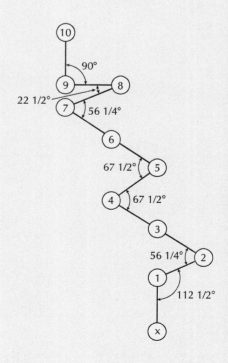

Chart 1 Agility Rating Scale

Classification	Men	Women
Excellent	15.8 or faster	17.4 or faster
Very good	16.7–15.9	18.6–17.5
Good	18.6–16.8	22.3–18.7
Fair	18.8–18.7	23.4–22.4
Poor	18.9 or slower	23.5 or slower

Source: Adams et al.

Chart 2 Balance Rating Scale

Rating	Score
Excellent	90–100
Very good	80–89
Good	70–79
Fair	60–69
Poor	50–59

Chart 3 Coordination Rating Scale

Classification	Men	Women
Excellent	14–15	13–15
Very good	11–13	10–12
Good	5–10	4–9
Fair	3–4	2–3
Poor	0–2	0–1

III. Evaluating Coordination: The Stick Test of Coordination

The stick test of coordination requires you to juggle three wooden sticks. The sticks are used to perform a one-half flip and a full flip, as shown in the illustrations.

1. *One-half flip.* Hold two 24-inch (½ inch in diameter) dowel rods, one in each hand. Support a third rod of the same size across the other two. Toss the supported rod in the air, so that it makes a half turn. Catch the thrown rod with the two held rods.
2. *Full flip.* Perform the preceding task, letting the supported rod turn a full flip.

The test is performed as follows:

1. Practice the half-flip and full flip several times before taking the test.
2. When you are ready, attempt a half-flip five times. Score 1 point for each successful attempt.
3. When you are ready, attempt the full flip five times. Score 2 points for each successful attempt.

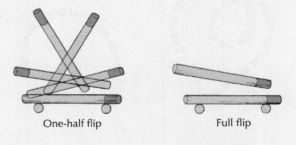

One-half flip   Full flip

Hand position

IV. Evaluating Power: The Vertical Jump Test

The test is performed as follows:

1. Hold a piece of chalk so its end is even with your fingertips.
2. Stand with both feet on the floor and your side to the wall and reach and mark as high as possible.
3. Jump upward with both feet as high as possible. Swing arms upward and make a chalk mark on a 5′ × 1′ wall chart marked off in half-inch horizontal lines placed 6 feet from the floor.
4. Measure the distance between the reaching height and the jumping height.
5. Your score is the best of three jumps.

Chart 4 Power Rating Scale

Classification	Men	Women
Excellent	25½″ or more	23½″ or more
Very good	21″–25″	19″–23″
Good	16 ½″–20½″	14½″–18½″
Fair	12½″–16″	10½″–14″
Poor	12″ or less	10″ or less

Metric conversions for this chart appear in Appendix A.

V. Evaluating Reaction Time: The Stick Drop Test

To perform the stick drop test of reaction time, you will need a yardstick, a table, a chair, and a partner to help with the test. To perform the test, follow this procedure:

1. Sit in the chair next to the table so that your elbow and lower arm rest on the table comfortably. The heel of your hand should rest on the table so that only your fingers and thumb extend beyond the edge of the table.
2. Your partner holds a yardstick at the top, allowing it to dangle between your thumb and fingers.
3. The yardstick should be held so that the 24-inch mark is even with your thumb and index finger. No part of your hand should touch the yardstick.
4. Without warning, your partner will drop the stick, and you will catch it with your thumb and index finger.
5. Your score is the number of inches read on the yardstick just above the thumb and index finger after you catch the yardstick.
6. Try the test three times. Your partner should be careful not to drop the stick at predictable time intervals, so that you cannot guess when it will be dropped. It is important that you react only to the dropping of the stick.
7. Use the middle of your three scores (for example: if your scores are 21, 18, and 19, your middle score is 19). The higher your score, the faster your reaction time.

Chart 5 Reaction Time Rating Scale

Classification	Score
Excellent	More than 21″
Very good	19″–21″
Good	16″–18¾″
Fair	13″–15¾″
Poor	Below 13″

Metric conversions for this chart appear in Appendix A.

VI. Evaluating Speed: 3-Second Run

To perform the running test of speed, it will be necessary to have a specially marked running course, a stopwatch, a whistle, and a partner to help you with the test. To perform the test, follow this procedure:

1. Mark a running course on a hard surface so that there is a starting line and a series of nine additional lines, each 2 yards apart, the first marked at a distance 10 yards from the starting line.

2. From a distance 1 or 2 yards behind the starting line, begin to run as fast as you can. As you cross the starting line, your partner starts a stopwatch.

3. Run as fast as you can until you hear the whistle, which your partner will blow exactly 3 seconds after the stopwatch is started. Your partner marks your location at the time the whistle was blown.

4. Your score is the distance you covered in 3 seconds. You may practice the test and take more than one trial if time allows. Use the better of your distances on the last two trials as your score.

Chart 6 Speed Rating Scale

Classification	Men	Women
Excellent	24–26 yards	22–26 yards
Very good	22–23 yards	20–21 yards
Good	18–21 yards	16–19 yards
Fair	16–17 yards	14–15 yards
Poor	Less than 16 yards	Less than 14 yards

Metric conversions for this chart appear in Appendix A.

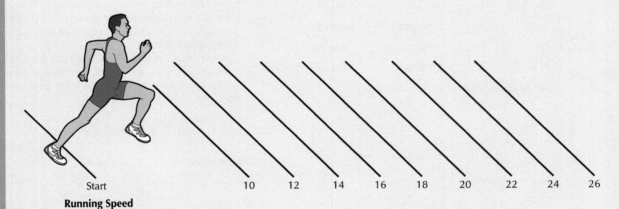

Start   10   12   14   16   18   20   22   24   26

Running Speed

Lab 12A Evaluating Skill-Related Physical Fitness

Name	Section	Date

Purpose: To help you evaluate your own skill-related fitness, including agility, balance, coordination, power, speed, and reaction time; this information may be of value in helping you decide which sports match your skill-related fitness abilities

Procedures

1. Read the direction for each of the skill-related fitness tests presented in *Lab Resource Materials.*
2. Take as many of the tests as possible, given the time and equipment available.
3. Be sure to warm up before and to cool down after the tests.
4. It is all right to practice the tests before trying them. However, you should decide ahead of time which trial you will use to test your skill-related fitness.
5. After completing the tests, write your scores in the appropriate places in the Results section.
6. Determine your rating for each of the tests from the rating charts in *Lab Resource Materials.*

Results

Place a check in the circle for each of the tests you completed.

Agility (Illinois run) ○

Balance (Bass test) ○

Coordination (stick test) ○

Power (vertical jump) ○

Reaction time (stick drop test) ○

Speed (3-second run) ○

Record your score and rating in the following spaces.

	Score	Rating	
Agility			(Chart 1)
Balance			(Chart 2)
Coordination			(Chart 3)
Power			(Chart 4)
Reaction time			(Chart 5)
Speed			(Chart 6)

Lab 12A

Evaluating Skill-Related Physical Fitness

Evaluating Skill-Related Physical Fitness

Conclusions and Implications: In two or three paragraphs, discuss the results of your skill-related fitness tests. Comment on the areas in which you did well or did not do well, the meaning of these findings, and the implications of the results, with specific reference to the activities you will perform in the future.

Lab 12B Identifying Symptoms of Overtraining

Name _____ **Section** _____ **Date** _____

Purpose: To help you identify the symptoms of overtraining

Procedures

1. Answer the questions concerning overtraining syndrome in the Results section. If you are in training, rate yourself; if not, evaluate a person you know who is in training. As an alternative, you may evaluate a person who was formerly in training (and who experienced symptoms) or evaluate yourself when you were in training (if you trained for performance in the past).
2. Use Chart 1 (below) to rate the person (yourself or another person) who is (or was) in training.
3. Use Chart 2 (page 288) to identify some strategies you can try to treat or prevent overtraining syndrome.
4. Answer the questions in the Conclusions and Implications section.

Results

Answer "Yes" (place a check in the circle) to any of the questions relating to overtraining symptoms you (or the person you are evaluating) experienced.

○ 1. Has performance decreased dramatically in the last week or two?

○ 2. Is there evidence of depression?

○ 3. Is there evidence of atypical anger?

○ 4. Is there evidence of atypical anxiety?

○ 5. Is there evidence of general fatigue that is not typical?

○ 6. Is there general lack of vigor or loss of energy?

○ 7. Have sleeping patterns changed (inability to sleep well)?

○ 8. Is there evidence of heaviness of the arms and/or legs?

○ 9. Is there evidence of loss of appetite?

○ 10. Is there a lack of interest in training?

Chart 1 Ratings for Overtraining Syndrome

Number of "Yes" Answers	Rating
9–10	Overtraining syndrome is very likely present. Seek help.
6–8	Person is at risk for overtraining syndrome if it is not already present. Seek help to prevent additional symptoms.
3–5	Some signs of overtraining syndrome are present. Consider methods of preventing further symptoms.
0–2	Overtraining syndrome is not present, but attention should be paid to the few symptoms that do exist.

Conclusions and Implications

Chart 2 lists some of the strategies that may help eliminate or prevent overtraining syndrome. Check the strategies that you think would be (or would have been) most useful to the person you evaluated.

Chart 2 Strategies for Treating or Preventing Overtraining Syndrome

○   1. Consider a break from training.

○   2. Taper the program to help reduce symptoms.

○   3. Seek help to redesign the training program.

○   4. Alter your diet.

○   5. Evaluate other stressors that may be producing symptoms.

○   6. Reset performance goals.

○   7. Talk to someone about problems.

○   8. Have a medical checkup to be sure there is no medical problem.

○   9. If you have a coach, consider a talk with him or her.

○   10. Add fluids to help prevent performance problems from dehydration.

Discuss overtraining syndrome in general. Elaborate on one or two of the strategies in Chart 2 that you think would be (or would have been) most effective in treating or preventing overtraining syndrome for the person you evaluated.

Nutrition and Body Composition

Lab Resource Materials: Evaluating Body Fat

General Information about Skinfold Measurements

It is important to use a consistent procedure for "drawing up" or "pinching up" a skinfold and making the measurement with the calipers. The following procedures should be used for each skinfold site.

1. Lay the calipers down on a nearby table. Use the thumbs and index fingers of both hands to draw up a skinfold, or layer of skin and fat. The fingers and thumbs of the two hands should be about 1 inch apart, or 1/2 inch on each side of the location where the measurement is to be made.

2. The skinfolds are normally drawn up in a vertical line rather than a horizontal line. However, if the skin naturally aligns itself less than vertical, the measurement should be done on the natural line of the skinfold, rather than on the vertical.

3. Do not pinch the skinfold too hard. Draw it up so that your thumbs and fingers are not compressing the skinfold.

4. Once the skinfold is drawn up, let go with your right hand and pick up the calipers. Open the jaws of the calipers and place them over the location of the skinfold to be measured and 1/2 inch from your left index finger and thumb. Allow the tips, or jaw faces, of the calipers to close on the skinfold at a level about where the skin would be normally.

5. Let the reading on the calipers settle for 2 or 3 seconds; then note the thickness of the skinfold in millimeters.

6. Three measurements should be taken at each location. Use the middle of the three values to determine your measurement. For example, if you had values of 10, 11, and 9, your measurement for that location would be 10. If the three measures vary by more than 3 millimeters from the lowest to the highest, you may want to take additional measurements.

Skinfold Measurement Methods

You will be exposed to two methods of using skinfolds. The first method (FITNESSGRAM) uses the same sites for men and women. It was originally developed for use with schoolchildren but has since been modified for adults. The second method (Jackson-Pollock) is the most widely used method. It uses different sites for men and women and considers your age in estimating your body fat percentage. You are encouraged to try both methods.

Calculating Fatness from Skinfolds (FITNESSGRAM Method)

1. Sum the three skinfolds (triceps, abdominal, and calf) for men and women. Use horizontal abdominal measure.

2. Use the skinfold sum and the appropriate column (men or women) to determine your percent fat using Chart 1. Locate your sum of skinfold in the left column at the top of the chart. Your estimated body fat percentage is located where the values intersect.

3. Use the Standards for Body Fatness (Chart 2) to determine your fatness rating.

FITNESSGRAM Locations (Men and Women)

Triceps

Make a mark on the back of the right arm, one-half the distance between the tip of the shoulder and the tip of the elbow. Make the measurement at this location.

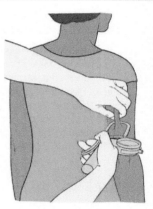

Abdominal

Make a mark on the skin approximately 1 inch to the right of the navel. Unlike the Jackson-Pollock method (done vertically), make a horizontal measurement.

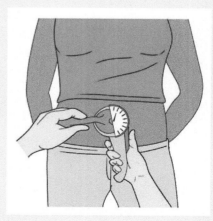

FITNESSGRAM Locations *(continued)*

Calf skinfold

Make a mark on the inside of the calf of the right leg at the level of the largest calf size (girth). Place the foot on a chair or other elevation so that the knee is kept at approximately 90 degrees. Make a vertical measurement at the mark.

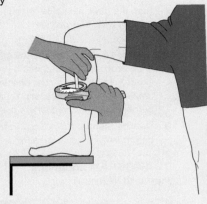

Self-Measured Triceps Skinfold

This measurement is made on the left arm so that the calipers can easily be read. Hold the arm straight at shoulder height. Make a fist with the thumb faced upward. Place the fist against a wall. With the right hand, place the calipers over the skinfold as it "hangs freely" on the back of the tricep (halfway from the tip of the shoulder to the elbow).

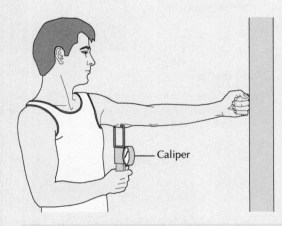

Caliper

Chart 1 Percent Fat for Sum of Triceps, Abdominal, and Calf Skinfolds (Fitnessgram)

Men		Women	
Sum of Skinfolds	Percent Fat	Sum of Skinfolds	Percent Fat
8–10	3.2	23–25	16.8
11–13	4.1	26–28	17.7
14–46	5.0	29–31	18.5
17–19	6.0	32–34	19.4
20–22	6.0	35–37	20.2
23–25	7.8	38–40	21.0
26–28	8.7	41–43	21.9
29–31	9.7	44–46	22.7
32–34	10.6	47–49	23.5
35–37	11.5	50–52	24.4
38–40	12.5	53–55	25.2
41–43	13.4	56–58	26.1
44–46	14.3	59–61	26.9
47–49	15.2	62–64	27.7
50–52	16.2	65–67	28.6
53–55	17.1	68–70	29.4
56–58	18.0	71–73	30.2
59–61	18.9	74–76	31.1
62–64	19.9	77–79	31.9
65–67	20.8	80–82	32.7
68–70	21.7	83–85	33.6
71–73	22.6	86–88	34.4
74–76	23.6	89–91	35.5
77–79	24.5	92–94	36.1
80–82	25.4	95–97	36.9
83–85	26.4	98–100	37.8
86–88	27.3	101–103	38.6
89–91	28.2	104–106	39.4
92–94	29.1	107–109	40.3
95–97	30.1	110–112	41.1
98–100	31.0	113–115	42.0
101–103	31.9	116–118	42.8
104–106	32.8	119–121	43.6
107–109	33.8	122–124	44.5
110–112	34.7	125–127	45.3
113–115	35.6	128–130	46.1
116–118	36.6	131–133	47.0
119–121	37.5	134–136	47.8
122–124	38.4	137–139	48.7
125–127	39.3	140–142	49.5

Chart 2 Standards for Body Fatness (Percent Body Fat)

	Too Low	Borderline	(Healthy) Good Fitness	Marginal	(At Risk) Overfat
	Below Essential Fat Levels	Unhealthy for Many People	Optimal for Good Health	Associated with Some Health Problems	Unhealthy
Males	No less than 5%	6–9%	10–20%	21–25%	>25%
Females	No less than 10%	11–16%	17–28%	29–35%	>35%

Calculating Fatness from Skinfolds (Jackson-Pollock Method)

1. Sum three skinfolds (tricep, iliac crest, and thigh for women; chest, abdominal [vertical], and thigh for men).

2. Use the skinfold sum and your age to determine your percent fat using Chart 3 for women and Chart 4 for men. Locate your sum of skinfold in the left column and your age at the top of the chart. Your estimated body fat percentage is located where the values intersect.

3. Use the Standards for Body Fatness (Chart 2) to determine your fatness rating.

Jackson-Pollock Locations (Women)

Triceps

Same as FITNESSGRAM (see page 305).

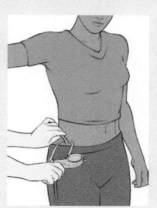

Iliac crest

Make a mark at the top front of the iliac crest. This skinfold is taken diagonally because of the natural line of the skin.

Thigh

Make a mark on the front of the thigh midway between the hip and the knee. Make the measurement vertically at this location.

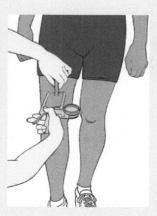

Jackson-Pollock Locations (Men)

Chest

Make a mark above and to the right of the right nipple (one-half the distance from the midline of the side and the nipple). The measurement at this location is often done on the diagonal because of the natural line of the skin.

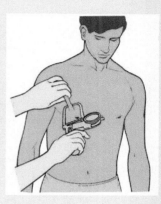

Abdominal

Make a mark on the skin approximately 1 inch to the right of the navel. Make a vertical measure for the Jackson-Pollock method and horizontally for the FITNESSGRAM method.

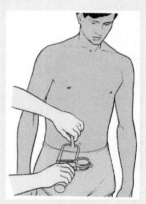

Thigh

Same as for women.

Note: Research has identified other methods that can also be used to calculate body fatness using skinfold measurements. See below.

- Ball, S., Altena, T., and P. Swan. 2004. Accuracy of anthropometry compared to dual energy x-ray absorptiometry: A new generalizable equation for men. *European Journal of Clinical Nutrition* 58:1525–1531.

- Ball, S., Swan, P., and R. Desimone. 2004. Comparison of anthropometry compared to dual energy x-ray absorptiometry: A new generalizable equation for women. *Research Quarterly for Exercise and Sports* 75:248–258.

Chart 3 Percent Fat for Women (Jackson-Pollock: Sum of Triceps, Iliac Crest, and Thigh Skinfolds)

Sum of Skinfolds (mm)	Age to the Last Year								
	22 and Under	23 to 27	28 to 32	33 to 37	38 to 42	43 to 47	48 to 52	53 to 57	Over 57
23–25	9.7	9.9	10.2	10.4	10.7	10.9	11.2	11.4	11.7
26–28	11.0	11.2	11.5	11.7	12.0	12.3	12.5	12.7	13.0
29–31	12.3	12.5	12.8	13.0	13.3	13.5	13.8	14.0	14.3
32–34	13.6	13.8	14.0	14.3	14.5	14.8	15.0	15.3	15.5
35–37	14.8	15.0	15.3	15.5	15.8	16.0	16.3	16.5	16.8
38–40	16.0	16.3	16.5	16.7	17.0	17.2	17.5	17.7	18.0
41–43	17.2	17.4	17.7	17.9	18.2	18.4	18.7	18.9	19.2
44–46	18.3	18.6	18.8	19.1	19.3	19.6	19.8	20.1	20.3
47–49	19.5	19.7	20.0	20.2	20.5	20.7	21.0	21.2	21.5
50–52	20.6	20.8	21.1	21.3	21.6	21.8	22.1	22.3	22.6
53–55	21.7	21.9	22.1	22.4	22.6	22.9	23.1	23.4	23.6
56–58	22.7	23.0	23.2	23.4	23.7	23.9	24.2	24.4	24.7
59–61	23.7	24.0	24.2	24.5	24.7	25.0	25.2	25.5	25.7
62–64	24.7	25.0	25.2	25.5	25.7	26.0	26.2	26.4	26.7
65–67	25.7	25.9	26.2	26.4	26.7	26.9	27.2	27.4	27.7
68–70	26.6	26.9	27.1	27.4	27.6	27.9	28.1	28.4	28.6
71–73	27.5	27.8	28.0	28.3	28.5	28.8	28.0	29.3	29.5
74–76	28.4	28.7	28.9	29.2	29.4	29.7	29.9	30.2	30.4
77–79	29.3	29.5	29.8	30.0	30.3	30.5	30.8	31.0	31.3
80–82	30.1	30.4	30.6	30.9	31.1	31.4	31.6	31.9	32.1
83–85	30.9	31.2	31.4	31.7	31.9	32.2	32.4	32.7	32.9
86–88	31.7	32.0	32.2	32.5	32.7	32.9	33.2	33.4	33.7
89–91	32.5	32.7	33.0	33.2	33.5	33.7	33.9	34.2	34.4
92–94	33.2	33.4	33.7	33.9	34.2	34.4	34.7	34.9	35.2
95–97	33.9	34.1	34.4	34.6	34.9	35.1	35.4	35.6	35.9
98–100	34.6	34.8	35.21	35.3	35.5	35.8	36.0	36.3	36.5
101–103	35.3	35.4	35.7	35.9	36.2	36.4	36.7	36.9	37.2
104–106	35.8	36.1	36.3	36.6	36.8	37.1	37.3	37.5	37.8
107–109	36.4	36.7	36.9	37.1	37.4	37.6	37.9	38.1	38.4
110–112	37.0	37.2	37.5	37.7	38.0	38.2	38.5	38.7	38.9
113–115	37.5	37.8	38.0	38.2	38.5	38.7	39.0	39.2	39.5
116–118	38.0	38.3	38.5	38.8	39.0	39.3	39.5	39.7	40.0
119–121	38.5	38.7	39.0	39.2	39.5	39.7	40.0	40.2	40.5
122–124	39.0	39.2	39.4	39.7	39.9	40.2	40.4	40.7	40.9
125–127	39.4	39.6	39.9	40.1	40.4	40.6	40.9	41.1	41.4
128–130	39.8	40.0	40.3	40.5	40.8	41.0	41.3	41.5	41.8

Source: Baumgartner and Jackson.

Note: Percent fat calculated by the formula by Siri. Percent fat = $[(4.95/BD) - 4.5] \times 100$, where BD = body density.

Lab Resource Materials

Evaluating Body Fat

Chart 4 Percent Fat for Men (Jackson-Pollock: Sum of Thigh, Chest, and Abdominal Skinfolds)

Sum of Skinfolds (mm)	Age to the Last Year								
	22 and Under	23 to 27	28 to 32	33 to 37	38 to 42	43 to 47	48 to 52	53 to 57	Over 57
8–10	1.3	1.8	2.3	2.9	3.4	3.9	4.5	5.0	5.5
11–13	2.2	2.8	3.3	3.9	4.4	4.9	5.5	6.0	6.5
14–16	3.2	3.8	4.3	4.8	5.4	5.9	6.4	7.0	7.5
17–19	4.2	4.7	5.3	5.8	6.3	6.9	7.4	8.0	8.5
20–22	5.1	5.7	6.2	6.8	7.3	7.9	8.4	8.9	9.5
23–25	6.1	6.6	7.2	7.7	8.3	8.8	9.4	9.9	10.5
26–28	7.0	7.6	8.1	8.7	9.2	9.8	10.3	10.9	11.4
29–31	8.0	8.5	9.1	9.6	10.2	10.7	11.3	11.8	12.4
32–34	8.9	9.4	10.0	10.5	11.1	11.6	12.2	12.8	13.3
35–37	9.8	10.4	10.9	11.5	12.0	12.6	13.1	13.7	14.3
38–40	10.7	11.3	11.8	12.4	12.9	13.5	14.1	14.6	15.2
41–43	11.6	12.2	12.7	13.3	13.8	14.4	15.0	15.5	16.1
44–46	12.5	13.1	13.6	14.2	14.7	15.3	15.9	16.4	17.0
47–49	13.4	13.9	14.5	15.1	15.6	16.2	16.8	17.3	17.9
50–52	14.3	14.8	15.4	15.9	16.5	17.1	17.6	18.1	18.8
53–55	15.1	15.7	16.2	16.8	17.4	17.9	18.5	18.2	19.7
56–58	16.0	16.5	17.1	17.7	18.2	18.8	19.4	20.0	20.5
59–61	16.9	17.4	17.9	18.5	19.1	19.7	20.2	20.8	21.4
62–64	17.6	18.2	18.8	19.4	19.9	20.5	21.1	21.7	22.2
65–67	18.5	19.0	19.6	20.2	20.8	21.3	21.9	22.5	23.1
68–70	19.3	19.9	20.4	21.0	21.6	22.2	22.7	23.3	23.9
71–73	20.1	20.7	21.2	21.8	22.4	23.0	23.6	24.1	24.7
74–76	20.9	21.5	22.0	22.6	23.2	23.8	24.4	25.0	25.5
77–79	21.7	22.2	22.8	23.4	24.0	24.6	25.2	25.8	26.3
80–82	22.4	23.0	23.6	24.2	24.8	25.4	25.9	26.5	27.1
83–85	23.2	23.8	24.4	25.0	25.5	26.1	26.7	27.3	27.9
86–88	24.0	24.5	25.1	25.5	26.3	26.9	27.5	28.1	28.7
89–91	24.7	25.3	25.9	25.7	27.1	27.6	28.2	28.8	29.4
92–94	25.4	26.0	26.6	27.2	27.8	28.4	29.0	29.6	30.2
95–97	26.1	26.7	27.3	27.9	28.5	29.1	29.7	30.3	30.9
98–100	26.9	27.4	28.0	28.6	29.2	29.8	30.4	31.0	31.6
101–103	27.5	28.1	28.7	29.3	29.9	30.5	31.1	31.7	32.3
104–106	28.2	28.8	29.4	30.0	30.6	31.2	31.8	32.4	33.0
107–109	28.9	29.5	30.1	30.7	31.3	31.9	32.5	33.1	33.7
110–112	29.6	30.2	30.8	31.4	32.0	32.6	33.2	33.8	34.4
113–115	30.2	30.8	31.4	32.0	32.6	33.2	33.8	34.5	35.1
116–118	30.9	31.5	32.1	32.7	33.3	33.9	34.5	35.1	35.7
119–121	31.5	32.1	32.7	33.3	33.9	34.5	35.1	35.7	36.4
122–124	32.1	32.7	33.3	33.9	34.5	35.1	35.8	36.4	37.0
125–127	32.7	33.3	33.9	34.5	35.1	35.8	36.4	37.0	37.6

Source: Baumgartner and Jackson.

Note: Percent fat calculated by the formula by Siri. Percent fat = [(4.95/BD) − 4.5] × 100, where BD = body density.

Calculating Fatness from Self-Measured Skinfolds

1. Use either the Jackson-Pollock or Fitnessgram method, but make the measures on yourself rather than have a partner do the measures. When doing the triceps measure, use the self-measurement technique for men and women. (See page 306.)
2. Calculate fatness using the methods described previously.

Height-Weight Measurements

1. *Height*—Measure your height in inches or centimeters. Take the measurement without shoes, but add 2.5 centimeters or 1 inch to measurements, as the charts include heel height.

2. *Weight*—Measure your weight in pounds or kilograms without clothes. Add 3 pounds or 1.4 kilograms because the charts include the weight of clothes. If weight must be taken with clothes on, wear indoor clothing that weighs 3 pounds, or 1.4 kilograms.

3. Determine your frame size using the elbow breadth. The measurement is most accurate when done with a broad-based sliding caliper. However, it can be done using skinfold calipers or can be estimated with a metric ruler. The right arm is measured when it is elevated with the elbow bent at 90 degrees and the upper arm horizontal. The back of the hand should face the person making the measurement. Using the calipers, measure the distance between the epicondyles of the humerus (inside and outside bony points of the elbow). Measure to the nearest millimeter (1/10 centimeter). If a caliper is not available, place the thumb and the index finger of the left hand on the epicondyles of the humerus and measure the distance between the fingers with a metric ruler. Use your height and elbow breadth in centimeters to determine your frame size (Chart 5); you need not repeat this procedure each time you use a height and weight chart.

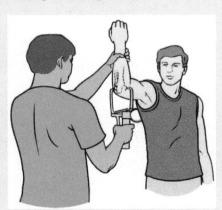

4. Use Chart 6 to determine your healthy weight range. The new healthy weight range charts do not account for frame size. However, you may want to consider frame size when determining a personal weight within the healthy weight range. People with a larger frame size typically can carry more weight within the range than can those with a smaller frame size.

Chart 5 Frame Size Determined from Elbow Breadth (mm)

Height	Elbow Breadth (mm)		
	Small Frame	Medium Frame	Large Frame
Males			
5'2 1/2" or less	<64	64–72	>72
5'3"–5'6 ½"	<67	67–74	>74
5'7"–5'10 ½"	<69	69–76	>76
5'11"–6'2 ½"	<71	71–78	>78
6'3" or more	<74	74–81	>81
Females			
4'10 ½" or less	<56	56–64	>64
4'11"–5'2 ½"	<58	58–65	>65
5'3"–5'6 ½"	<59	59–66	>66
5'7"–5'10 ½"	<61	61–68	>69
5'11" or more	<62	62–69	>69

Source: Metropolitan Life Insurance Company.
Height is given including 1-inch heels.

Chart 6 Healthy Weight Ranges for Adult Women and Men

Height			Height		
Feet	Inches	Pounds	Feet	Inches	Pounds
4	10	91–119	5	9	129–169
4	11	94–124	5	10	132–174
5	0	97–128	5	11	136–179
5	1	101–132	6	0	140–184
5	2	104–137	6	1	144–189
5	3	107–141	6	2	148–195
5	4	111–146	6	3	152–200
5	5	114–150	6	4	156–205
5	6	118–155	6	5	160–211
5	7	121–160	6	6	164–216
5	8	125–164			

Source: U.S. Department of Agriculture and Department of Health and Human Services.

Chart 7 Body Mass Index (BMI)

Height	100	105	110	115	120	125	130	135	140	145	150	155	160	165	170	175	180	185	190	195	200	205	210	215	220	225	230	235	240	245	250
5'0"	20	21	21	22	23	24	25	26	27	28	29	30	31	32	33	34	35	36	37	38	39	40	41	42	43	44	45	46	47	48	49
5'1"	19	20	21	22	23	24	25	26	26	27	28	29	30	31	32	33	34	35	36	37	38	39	40	41	42	43	43	44	45	46	47
5'2"	18	19	20	21	22	23	24	25	26	27	27	28	29	30	31	32	33	34	35	36	37	37	38	39	40	41	42	43	44	45	46
5'3"	18	19	19	20	21	22	23	24	25	26	27	27	28	29	30	31	32	33	34	35	35	36	37	38	39	40	41	42	43	43	44
5'4"	17	18	19	20	21	21	22	23	24	25	26	27	27	28	29	30	31	32	33	34	35	35	36	37	38	39	39	40	41	42	43
5'5"	17	17	18	19	20	21	22	22	23	24	25	26	27	27	28	29	30	31	32	32	33	34	35	36	37	37	38	39	40	41	42
5'6"	16	17	18	19	19	20	21	22	23	23	24	25	26	27	27	28	29	30	31	31	32	33	34	35	36	36	37	38	39	40	40
5'7"	16	16	17	18	19	20	20	21	22	23	23	24	25	26	27	27	28	29	30	31	31	32	33	34	34	35	36	37	38	38	39
5'8"	15	16	17	17	18	19	20	21	21	22	23	24	24	25	26	27	27	28	29	30	30	31	32	33	33	34	35	36	36	37	38
5'9"	15	15	16	17	18	19	19	20	21	21	22	23	24	24	25	26	27	27	28	29	30	30	31	32	32	33	34	35	35	36	37
5'10"	14	15	16	17	17	18	19	20	21	21	22	23	24	24	25	26	27	27	28	29	29	30	31	32	32	33	34	34	35	35	36
5'11"	14	15	15	16	17	17	18	19	20	20	21	22	22	23	24	24	25	26	26	27	28	29	29	30	31	31	32	33	33	34	35
6'0"	14	14	15	16	16	17	18	18	19	20	20	21	22	22	23	24	24	25	26	26	27	28	28	29	30	31	31	32	33	33	34
6'1"	13	14	15	15	16	16	17	18	18	19	20	20	21	22	22	23	24	24	25	26	26	27	28	28	29	30	30	31	32	32	33
6'2"	13	13	14	15	15	16	17	17	18	19	19	20	21	21	22	22	23	24	24	25	26	26	27	28	28	29	30	30	31	31	32
6'3"	12	13	14	14	15	15	16	16	17	17	18	19	19	20	21	21	22	22	23	24	24	25	26	26	27	27	28	29	29	30	31
6'4"	12	13	13	14	15	15	16	16	17	18	18	19	19	20	21	21	22	23	23	24	24	25	26	26	27	27	28	29	29	30	30

Weight

■ Low   ■ Normal (good fitness zone)   □ Overweight   □ Obese

Body Mass Index (BMI)

Use the steps listed below or use Chart 7 to calculate your BMI.

1. Divide your weight in pounds by 2.2 to determine your weight in kilograms.
2. Multiply your height in inches by 0.0254 to determine your height in meters.
3. Square your height in meters (multiply your height in meters by your height in meters).
4. Divide your weight in kilograms from step 1 by your height in meters squared from step 3.
5. If you use these steps to determine your BMI, use the Rating Scale for Body Mass Index (Chart 8) to obtain a rating for your BMI.

Chart 8 Rating Scale for Body Mass Index (BMI)

Classification	BMI
Obese (high risk)	Over 30
Overweight	25–30
Normal (good fitness zone)	17–24.9
Low	Less than 17

Note: An excessively low BMI is not desirable. Low BMI values can indicate eating disorders and other health problems.

Formula

$$BMI = \frac{\text{weight in kilograms (kg)}}{(\text{height in meters}) \times (\text{height in meters})}$$

$$BMI = \frac{\text{weight in pounds (lb)}}{(\text{height in inches}) \times (\text{height in inches})} \times 703$$

Determining the Waist-to-Hip Circumference Ratio

The waist-to-hip circumference ratio is recommended as the best available index for determining risk for disease associated with fat and weight distribution. Disease and death risk are associated with abdominal and upper body fatness. When a person has high fatness and a high waist-to-hip ratio, additional risks exist. The following steps should be taken in making measurements and calculating the waist-to-hip ratio.

1. Both measurements should be done with a nonelastic tape. Make the measurements while standing with the feet together and the arms at the sides, elevated only high enough to allow the measurements. Be sure the tape is horizontal and around the entire circumference. Record scores to the nearest millimeter or 1/16th of an inch. Use the same units of measure for both circumferences (millimeters or 1/16th of an inch). The tape should be pulled snugly but not to the point of causing an indentation in the skin.

2. Waist measurement—Measure at the natural waist (smallest waist circumference). If no natural waist exists, the measurement should be made at the level of the umbilicus. Measure at the end of a normal inhale.

3. *Hip measurement*—Measure at the maximum circumference of the buttocks. It is recommended that you wear thin-layered clothing (such as a swimming suit or underwear) that will not add significantly to the measurement.

4. Divide the hip measurement into the waist measurement or use the waist-to-hip nomogram (Chart 9) to determine your waist-to-hip ratio.

5. Use the Waist-to-Hip Ratio Rating Scale (Chart 10) to determine your rating for the waist-to-hip ratio.

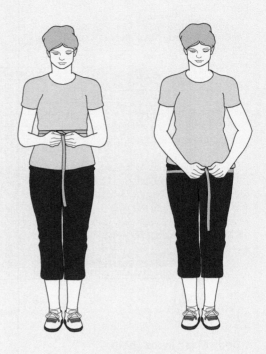

Chart 9 Waist-to-Hip Ratio Nomogram

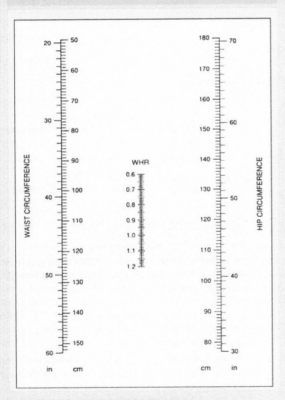

Note: Using a partner or mirror will aid you in keeping the tape horizontal.

Determining Disease Risk Based on BMI and Waist Circumference

Use Chart 11 to determine a BMI and Waist Circumference Rating. In the first column of Chart 11, locate your BMI. Locate your Waist Circumference in either column 2 or 3 depending on your age. Your rating is located at the point where the appropriate rows and columns intersect.

Chart 11 BMI and Waist Circumference Rating Scale

	Waist Circumference (in.)	
BMI	**Men 40 or less Women 34.5 or less**	**Men above 40 Women above 34.5**
Less than 18.5	Normal	Normal
18.5–24.9	Normal	Normal
25.0–29.9	Increased risk	High risk
30.0–34.9	High risk	Very high risk
35.0–39.9	Very high risk	Very high risk
40 or more	Extremely high risk	Extremely high risk

Source: Adapted from ACSM.

Chart 10 Waist-to-Hip Ratio Rating Scale

Classification	Men	Women
High risk	>1.0	>0.85
Moderately high risk	0.90–1.0	0.80–0.85
Lower risk	<0.90	<0.80

Lab 13A Evaluating Body Composition: Skinfold Measures

Name	**Section**	**Date**

Purpose: To estimate body fatness using two skinfold procedures; to compare measures made by an expert, by a partner, and by self-measurements; to learn the strengths and weaknesses of each technique; and to use the results to establish personal standards for evaluating body composition

General Procedures: Follow the specific procedures for the two self-assessment techniques. If possible, have one set of measurements made by an expert (instructor) for each of the two techniques. Next, work with a partner you trust. Have the partner make measurements at each site for both techniques. Finally, make self-measurements for each of the sites. If you are just learning a measurement technique, it is important to practice the skills of making the measurement. If you do measurements over time, use the same instrument (if possible) each time you measure. If your measurements vary widely, take more than one set until you get more consistent results.

If you have had an underwater weighing, a bioelectric impedance measurement, a near-infrared interactance measure, or some other body fatness measurement done recently, record your results below.

Measurement Technique   **% Body Fat**   **Rating**

1.

2.

Skinfold Measurements (Jackson-Pollock Method)

Procedures for Jackson-Pollock Method

1. Read the directions for the Jackson-Pollock method measurements in *Lab Resource Materials*.
2. If possible, observe a demonstration of the proper procedures for measuring skinfolds at each of the different locations before doing partner or self-measurements.
3. Make expert, partner, and self-measurements (see *Lab Resource Materials*). When doing the self-measure of the triceps, use the self-measurement technique described in *Lab Resource Materials* (women only).
4. Record each of the measurements in the Results section.
5. Calculate your body fatness from skinfolds by summing the appropriate skinfold values (chest, thigh, and abdominal for men; triceps, iliac crest, and thigh for women). Using your age and the sum of the appropriate skinfolds, determine your body fatness using Charts 3 and 4 in *Lab Resource Materials*.
6. Rate your fatness using Chart 2 in *Lab Resource Materials*.

Results for Jackson-Pollock Method

Skinfolds by an Expert (If Possible)	Skinfolds by Partner	Self-Measurements
Male	*Male*	*Male*
Chest	Chest	Chest
Thigh	Thigh	Thigh
Abdominal	Abdominal	Abdominal
Sum	Sum	Sum
% body fat	% body fat	% body fat
Rating	Rating	Rating
Female	*Female*	*Female*
Triceps	Triceps	Triceps
Iliac crest	Iliac crest	Iliac crest
Thigh	Thigh	Thigh
Sum	Sum	Sum
% body fat	% body fat	% body fat
Rating	Rating	Rating

Make a check by the statements that are true about your measurements.

☐ The person doing measurements has experience with these three skinfold measurements.

☐ Self-measurements were practiced until measurements became consistent.

☐ Results of several trials for each measure are consistent (do not vary more than 2–3 mm).

☐ You are not exceptionally low or exceptionally high in body fat.

The more checks you have, the more likely your measurements are accurate.

Skinfold Measurements (FITNESSGRAM Method)

Procedures for FITNESSGRAM Method

1. Read the directions for the FITNESSGRAM measurements in *Lab Resource Materials*.
2. Use the procedures as for the FITNESSGRAM method using the triceps, abdominal, and calf sites described in *Lab Resource Materials*. When doing the self-measure of the triceps, use the self-measurement technique shown earlier.
3. Calculate your body fatness from skinfolds by summing the appropriate skinfold values (same for both men and women). Using the sum of the appropriate skinfolds, determine your body fatness using Chart 1 in *Lab Resource Materials*.
4. Rate your fatness using Chart 2 in *Lab Resource Materials*.

Results for FITNESSGRAM Method

Skinfolds by an Expert (If Possible)		Skinfolds by Partner		Self-Measurements	
Triceps		Triceps		Triceps	
Abdominal		Abdominal		Abdominal	
Calf		Calf		Calf	
Sum		Sum		Sum	
% body fat		% body fat		% body fat	
Rating		Rating		Rating	

Make a check by the statements that are true about your measurements.

☐ The person doing measurements has experience with these three skinfold measurements.

☐ Self-measurements were practiced until measurements became consistent.

☐ Results of several trials for each measure are consistent (do not vary more than 2 to 3 mm).

☐ You are not exceptionally low or exceptionally high in body fat.

The more checks you have, the more likely your measurements are accurate.

Conclusions and Implications

In the space provided below, discuss your current body composition based on the two skinfold procedures and any other measures of body fatness you did. Note any discrepancies in the measurements and discuss which of the measurements you think provide the most useful information. To what extent do you think you need to alter your level of body fatness?

Lab 13B Evaluating Body Composition: Height, Weight, and Circumference Measures

Name	Section	Date

Purpose: To assess body composition using a variety of procedures, to learn the strengths and weaknesses of each technique, and to use the results to establish personal standards for evaluating body composition

General Procedures: Follow the specific procedures for the three self-assessment techniques. If possible, work with a partner you trust to help with measurements that you have difficulty making yourself. If you are just learning a measurement technique, it is important to practice the skills of making the measurement. If you do measurements over time, use the same instrument (if possible) each time you measure. If your measurements vary widely, take more than one set until you get more consistent results. If possible, have an expert make measurements on you using these procedures.

Height and Weight Measurements

Procedures

1. Read the directions for height and weight measurements in *Lab Resource Materials.*
2. Determine your healthy weight range using Chart 6 in *Lab Resource Materials.* You may want to use your elbow breadth (Chart 5). People with a smaller frame size should typically weigh less than those with a larger frame size within the healthy weight range. You may need the assistance of a partner to make the elbow breadth measurement.
3. Record your scores in the Results section.

Results

Weight [   ]   Healthy weight range [   ]

Height [   ]

Make a check by the statements that are true about your measurements.

[ ] You are confident in the accuracy of the scale you used.

[ ] You are confident that the height technique is accurate.

The more checks you have, the more likely your measurements are accurate.
If you are a very active person with a high amount of muscle, use this method with caution.

Body Mass Index

Procedures

1. Use the height and weight measures from above.
2. Determine your BMI score by using Chart 7 or the directions in *Lab Resource Materials.* Determine your rating using Chart 8.
3. Record your score and rating in the Results section.

Results

Body mass index [   ]   Rating [   ]

If you are a very active person with a high amount of muscle, use this method with caution.

Waist-to-Hip Ratio

Procedures

1. Measure your waist and hip circumferences using the procedures in *Lab Resource Materials*.
2. Divide your hip circumference into your waist circumference, or use Chart 9 in *Lab Resource Materials* to calculate your waist-to-hip ratio.
3. Determine your rating using Chart 10 in *Lab Resource Materials*.
4. Record your scores in the Results section.

Results

Waist circumference [＿＿＿]   Hip circumference [＿＿＿]   Waist-to-hip ratio [＿＿＿]   Rating [＿＿＿]

Make a check by the statements that are true about you.

[ ] I am a male 5´9″ or less and have a waist girth of 34 inches or more.

[ ] I am a male 5´10″ to 6´4″ and have a waist girth of 36 inches or more.

[ ] I am a male 6´5″ or more and have a waist girth of 38 inches or more.

[ ] I am a female 5´2″ or less and have a waist girth of 29 inches or more.

[ ] I am a female 5´3″ to 5´10″ and have a waist girth of 31 inches or more.

[ ] I am a female 5´11″ or more and have a waist girth of 33 inches or more.

If you checked one of the boxes above, the waist-to-hip ratio is especially relevant for you.

BMI and Waist Circumference Rating

Procedures

1. Locate your BMI and Waist Circumference from previous Results sections in this Lab.
2. Use these values to calculate your BMI and Waist Circumference Rating using Chart 11. Record the rating in the Results section.

Results

BMI and Waist Circumference Rating [＿＿＿]

Conclusions and Implications

In the space below, discuss your results for the height, weight, and circumference procedures. Note any discrepancies in the measurements. Indicate the strengths and weaknesses of the various methods. Which of the measures do you think provided you with the most useful information? If you also did the skinfold measures (Lab 13A), discuss your body composition based on all the information you have collected (skinfolds and height, weight, and circumference measures).

Lab 13C Determining Your Daily Energy Expenditure

Name	**Section**	**Date**

Purpose: To learn how many calories you expend in a day

Procedures

1. Estimate your basal metabolism using step 1 in the Results section in this Lab. First determine the number of minutes you sleep.
2. Monitor your activity expenditure for 1 day using Chart 1 (page 321). Record the number of 5-, 15-, and 30-minute blocks of time you perform each of the different types of physical activities (e.g., if an activity lasted 20 minutes, you would use one 15-minute block and one 5-minute block). Be sure to distinguish between moderate (Mod) and vigorous (Vig) intensity in your logging. If you perform an activity that is not listed, specify the activity on the line labeled "Other" and estimate if it is moderate or vigorous. You may want to keep copies of Chart 1 for future use. One extra copy is provided on page 322.
3. Sum the total number of minutes of moderate and vigorous activity. Determine your calories expended during moderate and vigorous activity using steps 2 and 3.
4. Determine your nonactive minutes using step 4. This is all time that is not spent sleeping or being active.
5. Determine your calories expended in nonactive minutes using step 5.
6. Determine your calories expended in a day using step 6.

Results

Daily Caloric Expenditure Estimates

Step 1:

Basal calories $= .0076 \times$ [Body wt. (lbs.)] $\times$ [Minutes of sleep] $=$ [Basal calories] (A)

Step 2:

Calories (moderate activity) $= .036 \times$ [Body wt. (lbs.)] $\times$ [Minutes of moderate activity] $=$ [Calories in moderate activity] (B)

Step 3:

Calories (vigorous activity) $= .053 \times$ [Body wt. (lbs.)] $\times$ [Minutes of vigorous activity] $=$ [Calories in vigorous activity] (C)

Step 4:

Minutes (nonactive) $= 1,440$ min $-$ [Minutes of sleep] $-$ [Minutes of moderate activity] $-$ [Minutes of vigorous activity] $=$ [Nonactive minutes]

Step 5:

Calories (rest and light activity) $= .011 \times$ [Body wt. (lbs.)] $\times$ [Nonactive minutes] $=$ [Calories in other activities] (D)

Step 6:

Calories expended (per day) $=$ [ ] (A) $+$ [ ] (B) $+$ [ ] (C) $+$ [ ] (D) $=$ [ ] **Daily calories**

Answer the following questions about your daily caloric expenditure estimate.

Yes   No

☐   ☐   Were the activities you performed similar to what you normally perform each day?

☐   ☐   Do you think your daily estimated caloric expenditure is an accurate estimate?

☐   ☐   Do you think you expend the correct number of calories in a typical day to maintain the body composition (body fat level) that is desirable for you?

Conclusions and Interpretations: In several paragraphs, discuss your daily caloric expenditure. Comment on your answers to the preceding questions. In addition, comment on whether you think you should modify your daily caloric expenditure for any reason.

Lab 13C

Determining Your Daily Energy Expenditure

Chart 1 Daily Activity Log

Day of Monitoring:

Physical Activity Category		5 Minutes	15 Minutes	30 Minutes	Minutes
Lifestyle Activity		1 2 3 4 5 6	1 2 3 4 5 6	1 2 3	
Dancing (general)	Mod				
Gardening	Mod				
Home repair/maintenance	Mod				
Occupation	Mod				
Walking/hiking	Mod				
Other:	Mod				
Aerobic Activity		1 2 3 4 5 6	1 2 3 4 5 6	1 2 3	
Aerobic dance (low-impact)	Mod / Vig				
Aerobic machines (rowing, stair, ski)	Mod / Vig				
Bicycling	Mod / Vig				
Running	Mod / Vig				
Skating (roller/ice)	Mod / Vig				
Swimming (laps)	Mod / Vig				
Other:	Mod / Vig				
Sport/Recreation Activity		1 2 3 4 5 6	1 2 3 4 5 6	1 2 3	
Basketball	Mod / Vig				
Bowling/billiards	Mod				
Golf	Mod				
Martial arts (judo, karate)	Mod / Vig				
Racquetball/tennis	Mod / Vig				
Soccer/hockey	Mod / Vig				
Softball/baseball	Mod				
Volleyball	Mod / Vig				
Other:	Mod				
Flexibility Activity		1 2 3 4 5 6	1 2 3 4 5 6	1 2 3	
Stretching	Mod				
Other:	Mod				
Strengthening Activity		1 2 3 4 5 6	1 2 3 4 5 6	1 2 3	
Calisthenics (push-ups/sit-ups)	Mod				
Resistance exercise	Mod				
Other:	Mod				

Minutes of moderate activity ☐

Minutes of vigorous activity ☐

Total minutes of activity ☐

Lab 13C

Determining Your Daily Energy Expenditure

Chart 1 Daily Activity Log

Day of Monitoring:

Physical Activity Category		5 Minutes	15 Minutes	30 Minutes	Minutes
Lifestyle Activity		1 2 3 4 5 6	1 2 3 4 5 6	1 2 3	
Dancing (general)	Mod				
Gardening	Mod				
Home repair/maintenance	Mod				
Occupation	Mod				
Walking/hiking	Mod				
Other:	Mod				
Aerobic Activity		1 2 3 4 5 6	1 2 3 4 5 6	1 2 3	
Aerobic dance (low-impact)	Mod / Vig				
Aerobic machines (rowing, stair, ski)	Mod / Vig				
Bicycling	Mod / Vig				
Running	Mod / Vig				
Skating (roller/ice)	Mod / Vig				
Swimming (laps)	Mod / Vig				
Other:	Mod / Vig				
Sport/Recreation Activity		1 2 3 4 5 6	1 2 3 4 5 6	1 2 3	
Basketball	Mod / Vig				
Bowling/billiards	Mod				
Golf	Mod				
Martial arts (judo, karate)	Mod / Vig				
Racquetball/tennis	Mod / Vig				
Soccer/hockey	Mod / Vig				
Softball/baseball	Mod				
Volleyball	Mod / Vig				
Other:	Mod				
Flexibility Activity		1 2 3 4 5 6	1 2 3 4 5 6	1 2 3	
Stretching	Mod				
Other:	Mod				
Strengthening Activity		1 2 3 4 5 6	1 2 3 4 5 6	1 2 3	
Calisthenics (push-ups/sit-ups)	Mod				
Resistance exercise	Mod				
Other:	Mod				

Minutes of moderate activity _____

Minutes of vigorous activity _____

Total minutes of activity _____

Lab 14A Nutrition Analysis

Name	**Section**	**Date**

Purpose: To learn to keep a dietary log, to determine the nutritional quality of your diet, to determine your average daily caloric intake, and to determine necessary changes in eating habits

Procedures

1. Record your dietary intake for 2 days using the Daily Diet Record sheets (see pages 345–346). Record intake for 1 weekday and 1 weekend day. You may wish to make copies of the record sheet for future use.
2. Include the actual foods eaten and the amount (size of portion in teaspoons, tablespoons, cups, ounces, or other standard units of measurement). Be sure to include all drinks (coffee, tea, soft drinks, etc.). Include *all* foods eaten, including sauces, gravies, dressings, toppings, spreads, and so on. Determine your caloric consumption for each of the 2 days. Use the calorie guides at the **myplate.gov** website to assist in evaluating your diet.
3. List the number of servings from each food group by each food choice.
4. Estimate the proportion of complex carbohydrate, simple carbohydrate, protein, and fat in each meal and in snacks, as well as for the total day.
5. Answer the questions in Chart 1 on page 344, using information for a typical day based on the Daily Diet Record sheets. Score 1 point for each "yes" answer. Then use Chart 2 to rate your dietary habits (circle rating).
6. Complete the Conclusions and Implications sections

Results

Record the number of calories consumed for each of the 2 days.

Weekday [   ] calories   Weekend [   ] calories

Conclusions and Implications: In several sentences, discuss your diet as recorded in this lab. Explain any changes in your eating habits that may be necessary. Comment on whether the days you surveyed are typical of your normal diet.

Lab 14A

Nutrition Analysis

Chart 1 Dietary Habits Questionnaire

Yes	No	Answer questions based on a typical day (use your Daily Diet Records to help).
○	○	1. Do you eat at least three healthy meals each day?
○	○	2. Do you eat a healthy breakfast?
○	○	3. Do you eat lunch regularly?
○	○	4. Does your diet contain 45 to 65 percent carbohydrates with a high concentration of fiber?*
○	○	5. Are less than one-fourth of the carbohydrates you eat simple carbohydrates?
○	○	6. Does your diet contain 10 to 35 percent protein?*
○	○	7. Does your diet contain 20 to 35 percent fat?*
○	○	8. Do you limit the amount of saturated fat in your diet (no more than 10 percent)?
○	○	9. Do you limit salt intake to acceptable amounts?
○	○	10. Do you get adequate amounts of vitamins in your diet without a supplement?
○	○	11. Do you typically eat 6 to 11 servings from the bread, cereal, rice, and pasta group of foods?
○	○	12. Do you typically eat 3 to 5 servings of vegetables?
○	○	13. Do you typically eat 2 to 4 servings of fruits?
○	○	14. Do you typically eat 2 to 3 servings from the milk, yogurt, and cheese group of foods?
○	○	15. Do you typically eat 2 to 3 servings from the meat, poultry, fish, beans, eggs, and nuts group of foods?
○	○	16. Do you drink adequate amounts of water?
○	○	17. Do you get adequate minerals in your diet without a supplement?
○	○	18. Do you limit your caffeine and alcohol consumption to acceptable levels?
○	○	19. Is your average caloric consumption reasonable for your body size and for the amount of calories you normally expend?
[ ]		Total number of "yes" answers

*Based on USDA standards.

Chart 2 Dietary Habits Rating Scale

Score	Rating
18–19	Very good
15–17	Good
13–14	Marginal
12 or less	Poor

Daily Diet Record

Day 1

Breakfast Food	Amount (cups, tsp., etc.)	Calories	Food Servings				Estimated Meal Calories %
			Bread/Cereal	Fruit/Veg.	Milk/Meat	Fat/Sweet	
							☐ % Protein
							☐ % Fat
							☐ % Complex carbohydrate
							☐ % Simple carbohydrate
							100% Total
Meal Total	✕						

Lunch Food	Amount (cups, tsp., etc.)	Calories	Food Servings				Estimated Meal Calories %
			Bread/Cereal	Fruit/Veg.	Milk/Meat	Fat/Sweet	
							☐ % Protein
							☐ % Fat
							☐ % Complex carbohydrate
							☐ % Simple carbohydrate
							100% Total
Meal Total	✕						

Dinner Food	Amount (cups, tsp., etc.)	Calories	Food Servings				Estimated Meal Calories %
			Bread/Cereal	Fruit/Veg.	Milk/Meat	Fat/Sweet	
							☐ % Protein
							☐ % Fat
							☐ % Complex carbohydrate
							☐ % Simple carbohydrate
							100% Total
Meal Total	✕						

Snack Food	Amount (cups, tsp., etc.)	Calories	Food Servings				Estimated Snack Calories %
			Bread/Cereal	Fruit/Veg.	Milk/Meat	Fat/Sweet	
							☐ % Protein
							☐ % Fat
							☐ % Complex carbohydrate
							☐ % Simple carbohydrate
							100% Total
Meal Total	✕						
Daily Totals	✕	Calories	Servings	Servings	Servings	Servings	

Estimated Daily Total Calories %
☐ % Protein
☐ % Fat
☐ % Complex carbohydrate
☐ % Simple carbohydrate
100% Total

Lab 14A

Nutrition Analysis

Daily Diet Record							

Day 2

Breakfast Food	Amount (cups, tsp., etc.)	Calories	Food Servings				Estimated Meal Calories %
			Bread/Cereal	Fruit/Veg.	Milk/Meat	Fat/Sweet	
							☐ % Protein
							☐ % Fat
							☐ % Complex carbohydrate
							☐ % Simple carbohydrate
							100% Total
Meal Total	✕						

Lunch Food	Amount (cups, tsp., etc.)	Calories	Food Servings				Estimated Meal Calories %
			Bread/Cereal	Fruit/Veg.	Milk/Meat	Fat/Sweet	
							☐ % Protein
							☐ % Fat
							☐ % Complex carbohydrate
							☐ % Simple carbohydrate
							100% Total
Meal Total	✕						

Dinner Food	Amount (cups, tsp., etc.)	Calories	Food Servings				Estimated Meal Calories %
			Bread/Cereal	Fruit/Veg.	Milk/Meat	Fat/Sweet	
							☐ % Protein
							☐ % Fat
							☐ % Complex carbohydrate
							☐ % Simple carbohydrate
							100% Total
Meal Total	✕						

Snack Food	Amount (cups, tsp., etc.)	Calories	Food Servings				Estimated Snack Calories %
			Bread/Cereal	Fruit/Veg.	Milk/Meat	Fat/Sweet	
							☐ % Protein
							☐ % Fat
							☐ % Complex carbohydrate
							☐ % Simple carbohydrate
							100% Total
Meal Total							**Estimated Daily Total Calories %**
Daily Totals	✕						☐ % Protein
		Calories	Servings	Servings	Servings	Servings	☐ % Fat
							☐ % Complex carbohydrate
							☐ % Simple carbohydrate
							100% Total

Lab 14B Selecting Nutritious Foods

| Name | | | Section | | Date | |

Purpose: To learn to select a nutritious diet, to determine the nutritive value of favorite foods, and to compare nutritious and favorite foods in terms of nutrient content

Procedures

1. Select a favorite breakfast, lunch, and dinner from the foods list in Appendix C. Include between-meal snacks with the nearest meal. If you cannot find foods you would normally choose, select those most similar to choices you might make.
2. Select a breakfast, lunch, and dinner from foods you feel would make the most nutritious meals. Include between-meal snacks with the nearest meal.
3. Record your "favorite foods" and "nutritious foods" on page 348. Record the calories for proteins, carbohydrates, and fats for each of the foods you choose.
4. Total each column for the "favorite" and the "nutritious" meals.
5. Determine the percentages of your total calories that are protein, carbohydrate, and fat by dividing each column total by the total number of calories consumed.
6. Comment on what you learned in the Conclusions and Implications section.

Results: Record your results below. Calculate percentage of calories from each source by dividing total calories into calories from each food source (protein, carbohydrates, or fat).

Food Selection Results

| Source | Favorite Foods | | Nutritious Foods | |
	Calories	% of Total Calories	Calories	% of Total Calories
Protein				
Carbohydrates				
Fat				
Total 100%		100%		100%

Conclusions and Implications: In several sentences, discuss the differences you found between your nutritious diet and your favorite diet. Discuss the quality of your nutritious diet as well as other things you learned from doing this lab.

Lab 14B

Selecting Nutritious Foods

"Favorite" versus "Nutritious" Food Choices for Three Daily Meals									
Breakfast Favorite	**Food Choices**				**Breakfast Nutritious**	**Food Choices**			
Food	Cal.	Pro. Cal.	Car. Cal.	Fat Cal.	Food	Cal.	Pro. Cal.	Car. Cal.	Fat Cal.
Totals					Totals				

Lunch Favorite	**Food Choices**				**Lunch Nutritious**	**Food Choices**			
Food	Cal.	Pro. Cal.	Car. Cal.	Fat Cal.	Food	Cal.	Pro. Cal.	Car. Cal.	Fat Cal.
Totals					Totals				

Dinner Favorite	**Food Choices**				**Dinner Nutritious**	**Food Choices**			
Food	Cal.	Pro. Cal.	Car. Cal.	Fat Cal.	Food	Cal.	Pro. Cal.	Car. Cal.	Fat Cal.
Totals					Totals				
Daily Totals (Calories)					Daily Totals (Calories)				
Daily % of Total Calories					Daily % of Total Calories				

Lab 15A Selecting Strategies for Managing Eating

Name	**Section**	**Date**

Purpose: To learn to select strategies for managing eating to control body fatness

Procedures

1. Read the strategies listed in Chart 1.
2. Check the box beside 5 to 10 of the strategies that you think will be most useful for you.
3. Answer the questions in the Conclusions and Implications section.

Chart 1 Strategies for Managing Eating to Control Body Fatness

✔	Check 5 to 10 strategies that you might use in the future.	✔	Check 5 to 10 strategies that you might use in the future.
	Shopping Strategies		**Eating on Special Occasions**
	Shop from a list.		Practice ways to refuse food.
	Shop with a friend.		Avoid tempting situations.
	Shop on a full stomach.		Eat before you go out.
	Check food labels.		Don't stand near food sources.
	Consider foods that take some time to prepare.		If you feel the urge to eat, find someone to talk to.
	Methods of Eating		**Strategies for Eating Out**
	When you eat, do nothing but eat. Don't watch television or read.		Limit deep-fat fried foods.
	Eat slowly.		Ask for information about food content.
	Do not eat food you do not want.		Limit use of condiments.
	Follow an eating schedule.		Choose low-fat foods (e.g., skim milk, low-fat yogurt).
	Do your eating in designated areas, such as kitchen or dining room only.		Choose chicken, fish, or lean meat.
	Leave the table after eating.		Order à la carte.
	Avoid second servings.		Ask early for a to-go box and divide portions.
	Limit servings of condiments.		If you eat desserts, avoid those with sauces or toppings.
	Limit servings of nonbasics, such as dessert, breads, and soft drinks.		**Eating at Home**
	Eat several meals of equal size rather than one big meal and two small ones.		Keep busy at times when you are at risk of overeating.
	Eating in the Work Environment		Store food out of sight.
	Bring your own food to work.		Avoid serving food to others between meals.
	Avoid snack machines.		If you snack, choose snacks with complex carbohydrates, such as carrot sticks or apple slices.
	If you eat out, plan your meal ahead of time.		Freeze leftovers to avoid the temptation of eating them between meals.
	Do not eat while working.		
	Avoid sharing foods from co-workers, such as birthday cakes.		
	Have activity breaks during the day.		
	Have water available to substitute for soft drinks.		
	Have low-calorie snacks to substitute for office snacks.		

Conclusions and Implications

1. In several sentences, discuss your need to use strategies for effective eating. Do you need to use them? Why or why not?

2. In several sentences, discuss the effectiveness of the strategies contained in Chart 1. Do you think they can be effective for people who have a problem controlling their body fatness?

3. In several sentences, discuss the value of using behavioral goals versus outcome goals when planning for fat loss.

Lab 15B Evaluating Fast-Food Options

Name		Section	Date

Purpose: To learn about the energy and fat content of fast food and how to make better choices when eating at fast-food restaurants

Procedures

1. Select a fast-food restaurant and a typical meal that you might order. Then use an online food calculator to determine total calories, fat calories, saturated fat intake, and cholesterol for each food item.
2. Record the values in Chart 2.
3. Sum the totals for the meal in Chart 2.
4. Record recommended daily values by selecting an amount from Chart 1. The estimate should be based on your estimated needs for the day.
5. Compute the percentage of the daily recommended amounts that you consume in the meal by dividing recommended amounts (step 4) into meal totals (step 3). Record percent of recommended daily amounts in Chart 2.
6. Answer the questions in the Conclusions and Implications section.

Chart 1 Recommended Daily Amounts of Fat, Saturated Fat, Cholesterol, and Sodium

	2,000 kcal	3,000 kcal
Total fat	65 g	97.5 g
Saturated fat	20 g	30 g
Cholesterol	300 mg	450 mg
Sodium	2,400 mg	3,600 g

Results

Chart 2 Listing of Foods Selected for the Meal

Food Item	Total Calories	Total Fat (g)	Saturated Fat (g)	Cholesterol (mg)
1.				
2.				
3.				
4.				
5.				
6.				
Total for meal (sum up each column)				
Recommended daily amount (record your values from Chart 1)				
% of recommended daily amount (record your % of recommended)				

Consult an online fast food calculator to estimate calorie content of menu choices (see www.fastfoodnutrition.org).

Conclusions and Implications:

1. Describe how often you eat at fast-food restaurants and indicate whether you would like to reduce how much fast food you consume.

2. Were you surprised at the amount of fat, saturated fat, and cholesterol in the meal you selected?

3. What could you do differently at fast-food restaurants to reduce your intake of fat, saturated fat, and cholesterol?

Stress Management

Lab 16A Evaluating Your Stress Level

Name	Section	Date

Purpose: To evaluate your stress during the past year and determine its implications

Procedures

1. Complete the Life Experience Survey (page 380) based on your experiences during the past year. This survey lists a number of life events that may be distressful or eustressful. Read all of the items. If you did not experience an event, leave the box blank. In the box after each event that you did experience, write a number ranging from –3 to +3 using the scale described in the directions. Extra blanks are provided to write in positive or negative events not listed. Some items apply only to males or females. Items 48 to 56 are only for current college students.
2. Add all of the negative numbers and record your score (distress) in the Results section. Add the positive numbers and record your score (eustress) in the Results section. Use all of the events in the past year.
3. Find your scores on Chart 1 and record your ratings in the Results section.
4. Interpret the results by discussing the Conclusions and Implications in the space provided.

Results

Sum of negative scores ☐ (distress)   Rating on negative scores ☐

Sum of positive scores ☐ (eustress)   Rating on positive scores ☐

Chart 1 Scale for Life Experiences and Stress

	Sum of Negative Scores (Distress)	Sum of Positive Scores (Eustress)
May need counseling	14+	
Above average	9–13	11+
Average	6–8	9–10
Below average	<6	<9

Scoring the Life Experience Survey

1. Add all of the negative scores to arrive at your own distress score (negative stress).
2. Add all of the positive scores to arrive at a eustress score (positive stress).

Conclusions and Implications: In several sentences, discuss your current stress rating and its implications.

Life Experience Survey

Directions: If you did not experience an event, leave the box next to the event empty. If you experienced an event, enter a number in the box based on how the event impacted your life. Use the following scale:

Extremely negative impact	= –3
Moderately negative impact	= –2
Somewhat negative impact	= –1
Neither positive nor negative impact	= 0
Somewhat positive impact	= +1
Moderately positive impact	= +2
Extremely positive impact	= +3

1. Marriage ☐
2. Detention in jail or comparable institution ☐
3. Death of spouse ☐
4. Major change in sleeping habits (much more or less sleep) ☐
5. Death of close family member:
   a. Mother ☐
   b. Father ☐
   c. Brother ☐
   d. Sister ☐
   e. Child ☐
   f. Grandmother ☐
   g. Grandfather ☐
   h. Other (specify) _____ ☐
6. Major change in eating habits (much more or much less food intake) ☐
7. Foreclosure on mortgage or loan ☐
8. Death of a close friend ☐
9. Outstanding personal achievement ☐
10. Minor law violation (traffic ticket, disturbing the peace, etc.) ☐
11. *Male:* Wife's/girlfriend's pregnancy ☐
    Female: Pregnancy ☐
12. Changed work situation (different working conditions, working hours, etc.) ☐
13. New job ☐
14. Serious illness or injury of close family member:
    a. Father ☐
    b. Mother ☐
    c. Sister ☐
    d. Brother ☐
    e. Grandfather ☐
    f. Grandmother ☐
    g. Spouse ☐
    h. Child ☐
    i. Other (specify) _____ ☐
15. Sexual difficulties ☐
16. Trouble with employer (in danger of losing job, being suspended, demoted, etc.) ☐
17. Trouble with in-laws ☐
18. Major change in financial status (a lot better off or a lot worse off) ☐
19. Major change in closeness of family members (decreased or increased closeness) ☐

20. Gaining a new family member (through birth, adoption, family member moving in, etc.) ☐
21. Change of residence ☐
22. Marital separation from mate (due to conflict) ☐
23. Major change in church activities (increased or decreased attendance) ☐
24. Marital reconciliation with mate ☐
25. Major change in number of arguments with spouse (a lot more or a lot fewer arguments) ☐
26. *Married male:* Change in wife's work outside the home (beginning work, ceasing work, changing to a new job) ☐
    Married female: Change in husband's work (loss of job, beginning new job, retirement, etc.) ☐
27. Major change in usual type and/or amount of recreation ☐
28. Borrowing more than $10,000 (buying a home, business, etc.) ☐
29. Borrowing less than $10,000 (buying car or TV, getting school loan, etc.) ☐
30. Being fired from job ☐
31. *Male:* Wife/girlfriend having abortion ☐
    Female: Having abortion ☐
32. Major personal illness or injury ☐
33. Major change in social activities, such as parties, movies, visiting (increased or decreased participation) ☐
34. Major change in living conditions of family (building new home, remodeling, deterioration of home or neighborhood, etc.) ☐
35. Divorce ☐
36. Serious injury or illness of close friend ☐
37. Retirement from work ☐
38. Son or daughter leaving home (due to marriage, college, etc.) ☐
39. Ending of formal schooling ☐
40. Separation from spouse (due to work, travel, etc.) ☐
41. Engagement ☐
42. Breaking up with boyfriend/girlfriend ☐
43. Leaving home for the first time ☐
44. Reconciliation with boyfriend/girlfriend ☐

Other recent experiences that have had an impact on your life: list and rate.

45. _____ ☐
46. _____ ☐
47. _____ ☐

For Students Only

48. Beginning new school experience at a higher academic level (college, graduate school, professional school, etc.) ☐
49. Changing to a new school at same academic level (undergraduate, graduate, etc.) ☐
50. Academic probation ☐
51. Being dismissed from dormitory or other residence ☐
52. Failing an important exam ☐
53. Changing a major ☐
54. Failing a course ☐
55. Dropping a course ☐
56. Joining a fraternity/sorority ☐

Source: **Sarason, Johnson, and Siegel.**

Lab 16B Evaluating Your Hardiness and Locus of Control

Name	Section	Date

Purpose: To evaluate your level of hardiness and locus of control and to help you identify the ways in which you appraise and respond to stressful situations

Procedures

1. Complete the Hardiness Questionnaire and the Locus of Control Questionnaire. Make an X over the circle that best describes what is true for you personally.
2. Compute the scale scores and record the values in the Results section.
3. Evaluate your scores using the Rating chart (Chart 1), and record your ratings in the Results section.
4. Interpret the results by answering the questions in the Conclusions and Implications section.

Hardiness Questionnaire

	Not True	Rarely True	Sometimes True	Often True	Score
1. I look forward to school and work on most days.	1	2	3	4	
2. Having too many choices in life makes me nervous.	4	3	2	1	
3. I know where my life is going and look forward to the future.	1	2	3	4	
4. I prefer not to get too involved in relationships.	4	3	2	1	
				Commitment Score, Sum 1–4	
5. My efforts at school and work will pay off in the long run.	1	2	3	4	
6. I just have to trust my life to fate to be successful.	4	3	2	1	
7. I believe that I can make a difference in the world.	1	2	3	4	
8. Being successful in life takes more luck and good breaks than effort.	4	3	2	1	
				Control Score, Sum 5–8	
9. I would be willing to work for less money if I could do something really challenging and interesting.	1	2	3	4	
10. I often get frustrated when my daily plans and schedule get altered.	4	3	2	1	
11. Experiencing new situations in life is important to me.	1	2	3	4	
12. I don't mind being bored.	4	3	2	1	
				Challenge Score, Sum 9–12	

Locus of Control Questionnaire

	Not True	Rarely True	Sometimes True	Often True	Score
13. Hard work usually pays off.	1	2	3	4	
14. Buying a lottery ticket is not worth the money.	1	2	3	4	
15. Even when I fail I keep trying.	1	2	3	4	
16. I am usually successful in what I do.	1	2	3	4	
17. I am in control of my own life.	1	2	3	4	
18. I make plans to be sure I am successful.	1	2	3	4	
19. I know where I stand with my friends.	1	2	3	4	
				Locus of Control, Sum 13–19	

Results

Hardiness

Commitment score [ ]

Control score [ ]

Challenge score [ ]

Hardiness score [ ]

Commitment rating [ ]

Control rating [ ]

Challenge rating [ ]

Hardiness rating [ ]

Locus of Control

Locus of Control score [ ]

Locus of Control rating [ ]

Chart 1 Rating Chart

Rating	Individual Hardiness Scale Scores	Total Hardiness Score	Locus of Control Score
High	14–16	40–48	24–28
Moderate	10–13	30–39	12–23
Low	<10	<30	<12

Conclusions and Implications

1. In several sentences, discuss your commitment, control, and challenge ratings, as well as your overall hardiness rating. Are they what you expected? Do you think they are true indications of your hardiness? Explain.

[ ]

2. In several sentences, discuss your locus of control rating. Is it what you expected (a high rating indicates an internal locus of control)? Do you think your rating is a realistic indicator of your locus of control? Explain.

[ ]

Lab 17A Time Management

Name	**Section**	**Date**

Purpose: To learn to manage time to meet personal priorities

Procedures

1. Follow the four steps outlined below.
2. Complete the Conclusions and Implications section.

Results

Step 1: Establishing Priorities

1. Check the circles that reflect your priorities in the list below. Add priorities as necessary.
2. Rate each of the priorities you checked. Use a 1 for highest priority, 2 for moderate priority, and 3 for low priority.

Check Priorities	Rating	Check Priorities	Rating	Check Priorities	Rating
◯ More time with family		◯ More time with boy/girlfriend		◯ More time with spouse	
◯ More time for leisure		◯ More time to relax		◯ More time to study	
◯ More time for work success		◯ More time for physical activity		◯ More time to improve myself	
◯ More time for other recreation		◯ Other _____		◯ Other _____	

Step 2: Monitor Current Time Use

1. On the following daily calendar, keep track of daily time expenditure.
2. Write in exactly what you did for each time block.

7–9 A.M.	9–11 A.M.	11 A.M.–1 P.M.	1–3 P.M.
3–5 P.M.	**5–7 P.M.**	**7–9 P.M.**	**9–11 P.M.**

Step 3: Analyze Your Current Time Use by Using the ABC Method (See Table 2 on page 387)

A Tasks That Must *Absolutely* Get Done	B Tasks That *Better* Get Done	C Tasks That *Could* Be Done

Step 4: Make a Schedule: Write in Your Planned Activities for the Day

Time	Activities	Time	Activities
6:00 A.M.		3:00 P.M.	
7:00 A.M.		4:00 P.M.	
8:00 A.M.		5:00 P.M.	
9:00 A.M.		6:00 P.M.	
10:00 A.M.		7:00 P.M.	
11:00 A.M.		8:00 P.M.	
12:00 P.M.		9:00 P.M.	
1:00 P.M.		10:00 P.M.	
2:00 P.M.		11:00 P.M.	

Conclusions and Implications: In several sentences, discuss how you might modify your schedule to find more time for important priorities.

Lab 17B Evaluating Coping Strategies

Name	**Section**	**Date**

Purpose: To learn how to use appropriate coping strategies that work best for you

Procedures

1. Think of five recent stressful experiences that caused you some concern, anxiety, or distress. Describe these situations in Chart 1. Then use Chart 2 to make a rating for changeability, severity, and duration. Assign one number for each category for each situation.
2. In Chart 3, place a check for each coping strategy that you used in coping with each of the five situations you described.
3. Answer the questions in the Conclusions and Implications section.

Results

Chart 1 Stressful Situations

Think of five different stressful situations. Appraise each situation and assign a score (changeability, severity, duration) using the scale in Chart 2.

Briefly describe the situation.	Changeability	Severity	Duration
1.			
2.			
3.			
4.			
5.			

Chart 2 Appraisal of the Stressful Situations

Use this chart to rate the five situations you described in Chart 1. Assign a number for changeability, severity, and duration for each situation in Chart 1.

	1	2	3	4	5
Was the situation changeable?	Completely within my control	Mostly within my control	Both in and out of my control	Mostly out of my control	Completely outside of my control
What was the severity of the stress?	Very minor	Fairly minor	Moderate	Fairly major	Very major
What was the duration of the stress?	Short-term (weeks)	Moderately short	Moderate (months)	Moderately long	Long (months to year)

Chart 3   Coping Strategies

Directions: Think about your response to the five stressful situations you recently experienced and check the strategies that you used in each situation. List use of other strategies as appropriate.

Coping Strategy	Situation 1	Situation 2	Situation 3	Situation 4	Situation 5
1. I apologized or corrected the problem as best I could.					
2. I ignored the problem and hoped that it would go away.					
3. I told myself to forget about it and grew as a person from the experience.					
4. I tried to make myself feel better by eating, drinking, or smoking.					
5. I prayed or sought spiritual meaning from the situation.					
6. I expressed anger to try to change the situation.					
7. I took active steps to make things work out better.					
8. I used music, images, or deep breathing to help me relax.					
9. I tried to keep my feelings to myself and kept moving forward.					
10. I pursued leisure or recreational activity to help me feel better.					
11. I talked to someone who could provide advice or help me with the problem.					
12. I talked to someone about what I was feeling or experiencing.					
13. Other _____					
14. Other _____					
15. Other _____					

Conclusions and Implications: In several sentences, discuss the coping strategies you used. What were the ones you used the most? Are these the ones you typically use? Were they effective? Would you consider other strategies in the future?

Lab 17C Relaxation Exercises

Name	**Section**	**Date**

Purpose: To gain experience with specific relaxation exercises and to evaluate their effectiveness

Procedures

1. Choose two of the relaxation exercises included in Chart 1 of this lab (see page 402) and read through the written instructions until you have a basic understanding of the exercises. Think through the specific aspects of the exercise until you have the process figured out.
2. Find a quiet place to try one of the exercises and follow the procedures as best you can. It is not possible to provide detailed instructions, but the information should be sufficient to give you a basic understanding of the exercises.
3. On another day try a different exercise.
4. Answer the questions in the Results section. Then complete the Conclusions and Implications section.

Results

1. Which of the two exercises did you try? (List them below.)

2. Have you done either of the exercises before?   ◯ Yes   ◯ No

3. Was one relaxation exercise more effective or better suited to you than the others? Which one?

Conclusions and Implications

In several sentences, discuss whether or not you feel that relaxation exercises will be a part of your wellness program. In what ways might you benefit from relaxation training? If you do not think you have a problem with relaxation, explain why.

Chart 1   Descriptions of Relaxation Exercises

A. Progressive Relaxation

Progressive relaxation uses active (conscious) mechanisms to achieve a state of relaxation. The technique involves alternating phases of muscle contraction (tension) and muscle relaxation (tension release). Muscle groups are activated one body segment at a time, incorporating all regions of the body by the end of the routine. Begin by lying on your back in a quiet place with eyes closed. Alternately contract and relax each of the muscles below—following the procedures described below. Begin with the dominant side of the body first; repeat on the nondominant side.

1. Hand and forearm—Make a fist.
2. Biceps—Flex elbows.
3. Triceps—Straighten arm.
4. Forehead—Raise your eyebrows and wrinkle forehead.
5. Cheeks and nose—Wrinkle nose and squint.
6. Jaws—Clench teeth.
7. Lips and tongue—Press lips together and tongue to roof of mouth, teeth apart.
8. Neck and throat—Tuck chin and push head backward against floor (if lying) or chair (if sitting).
9. Shoulder and upper back—Hunch shoulders to ears.
10. Abdomen—Suck abdomen inward.
11. Lower back—Arch back.
12. Thighs and buttocks—Squeeze buttocks together, push heels into floor (if lying) or chair rung (if sitting).
13. Calves—Pull instep and toes toward shins.
14. Toes—curl toes.

Muscle contraction phase: Inhale as you contract the designated muscle for 3–5 seconds. Use only a moderate level of tension.

Muscle relaxation phase: Exhale, relaxing the muscle and releasing tension for 6–10 seconds. Think of relaxation words such as warm, calm, peaceful, and serene.

Relax every muscle in your body at the end of the exercise.

Figure 3 ▶ Diaphragmatic breathing.

B. Diapraghmatic Breathing

This exercise will help improve awareness of using deep abdominal breathing over shallower chest-type breathing. To begin, lie on your back with knees bent and feet on the floor. Place your right hand over your abdomen and left hand over your chest. Your hands will be used to monitor breathing technique. Slowly inhale through the nose by allowing the abdomen to rise under your right hand. Concentrate on expanding the abdomen for 4 seconds. Continue inhaling another 2 seconds allowing the chest to rise under your left hand. Exhale through your mouth in reverse order (for about 8 seconds, or twice as long as inhalation). Relax the chest first, feeling it sink beneath the left hand and then the abdomen, allowing it to sink beneath the right hand. Repeat 4–5 times. Discontinue if you become light-headed.

C. Show Gun

This is a form of Qigong, a Chinese meditation technique. The basic principles of tai chi are to maintain balance, use the entire body to achieve movement, unite movement with awareness (mind) and breathing (chi), and to keep the body upright. Tai chi involves holding the body in specific positions, or "forms." To execute the basic form, stand straight, feet shoulder-width apart and parallel with one another. Your knees should be bent and turned outward slightly with knees over the foot. Your hands are on belly button with palms facing body (men place hands right on left and women left on right), fingers are straight, spread slightly and relaxed.

1. Bring arms in front of body at a 30-degree angle to the plane of the back, palms face downward. Reach up to shoulder height with arms moving up and to the sides. (Breathe in, allowing belly to move out as you raise arms upward.)
2. When hands reach shoulder height, turn palms up and move hands to head, allowing wrists to drop down. Imagine energy (chi) flowing from palms to top of head. (Continue breathing in.)
3. Imagine energy flowing down through a central line of the body. Follow the energy with hands, point fingers toward one another, palms down, move arms downward in front of the midline of face and chest. (Breathe out as arms lower.)
4. Two inches bellow belly button stop, cross palms, and move hands together.
5. Lower hands toward sides. (Complete breathing out.)
6. Repeat.

Lab 17D Evaluating Levels of Social Support

Name	Section	Date

Purpose: To evaluate your level of social support and to identify ways that you can find additional support

Procedures

1. Answer each question in Chart 1 by placing a check in the box below Not True, Somewhat True, or Very True. Place the number value of each answer in the score box to the right.
2. Sum the scores (in the smaller boxes) for each question to get subscale scores for the three social support areas.
3. Record your three subscores in the Results section on the next page. Total your subscores to get a total social support score.
4. Determine your ratings for each of the three social support subscores and for your total social support score using Chart 2 on the next page.
5. Answer the questions in the Conclusions and Implications section.

Chart 1 Social Support Questionnaire

These questions assess various aspects of social support. Base your answer on your actual degree of support, not on the type of support that you would like to have. Place a check in the space that best represents what is true for you.

Social Support Questions	Not True 1	Somewhat True 2	Very True 3	Score
1. I have close personal ties with my relatives.				
2. I have close relationships with a number of friends.				
3. I have a deep and meaningful relationship with a spouse or close friend.				
			Access to social support score:	
4. I have parents and relatives who take the time to listen and understand me.				
5. I have friends or co-workers whom I can confide in and trust when problems come up.				
6. I have a nonjudgmental spouse or close friend who supports me when I need help.				
			Degree of social support score:	
7. I feel comfortable asking others for advice or assistance.				
8. I have confidence in my social skills and enjoy opportunities for new social contacts.				
9. I am willing to open up and discuss my personal life with others.				
			Getting social support score:	

Results

Scores and Ratings

(Use Chart 2 to obtain ratings.)

Access to social support score [ ]   Rating [ ]

Degree of social support score [ ]   Rating [ ]

Getting social support score [ ]   Rating [ ]

Total social support score
(sum of three scores) [ ]   Rating [ ]

Chart 2 Rating Scale for Social Support

Rating	Item Scores	Total Score
High	8–9	24–27
Moderate	6–7	18–23
Low	Below 6	Below 18

Conclusions and Implications

1. In several sentences, discuss your overall social support. Do you think your scores and ratings are a true representation of your social support?

2. In several sentences, describe any changes you think you should make to improve your social support system. If you do not think change is necessary, explain why.

Making Informed Choices

Lab 18A Practicing Consumer Skills: Evaluating Products

Name	**Section**	**Date**

Purpose: To evaluate an exercise device, a book, a magazine article, an advertisement, a food supplement, or a website

Procedures

1. Evaluate an exercise device, a book, an article, a newspaper or magazine advertisement, a food supplement, or a website. Place an X in the circle by the item you choose to evaluate. Attach a copy if you evaluate an advertisement.
2. Read each of the 10 evaluation factors for the item you selected. Place an X in the circle by the factors that describe the item you are evaluating.
3. Total the number of X marks to determine a score for the item being evaluated. The higher the score, the more likely it is to be safe and/or effective.
4. Answer the questions in the Conclusions and Implications section.

Results

Directions: Place an X in the circle by the product you evaluated. Place an X over the circle by each true statement. Provide information about the product in the space provided.

Exercise Device

1. The exercise device requires effort consistent with the FIT formula.
2. The exercise device is safe and the exercise done using the device is safe.
3. There are no claims that the device uses exercise that is effortless.
4. Exercise using the device is fun or is a type that you might do regularly.
5. There are no claims using gimmick words, such as *tone, cellulite, quick,* or *spot fat reduction.*
6. The seller's credentials are sound.
7. The product does something for you that cannot be done without it.
8. You can return the device if you do not like it (the seller has been in business for a long time).
9. The cost of the product is justified by the potential benefits.
10. The device is easy to store or you have a place to permanently use the equipment without storing it.

Exercise Device

Name of device: _____

Description and manufacturer: _____

Book or Article

Author(s): _____

Journal article or book title: _____

Journal name or name of publisher: _____

Date of publication: _____

Advertisement

Source: _____

Book/Article/Advertisement

1. The credentials of the author are sound. He or she has a degree in an area related to the content of the book or magazine.*
2. The facts in the article are consistent with the facts described in this book.
3. The author does not claim "quick" or "miraculous" results.
4. There are no claims about the spot reduction of fat or other unfounded claims.
5. The author/advertisement is not selling a product.
6. Reputable experts are cited.
7. The article does not promote unsafe exercises or products.
8. New discoveries from exotic places are not cited.
9. The article/advertisement does not rely on testimonials by nonexpert, famous people.
10. The author/advertisement does not make claims that the AMA, the FDA, or another legitimate organization is trying to suppress information.

*Not applicable for advertisement.

Food Supplement

1. The seller is not the prime source of product information.

2. The seller has been in business for a long time and has a good reputation.

3. There is scientific evidence of product effectiveness.

4. There is clear evidence about the side effects of the active ingredients.

5. The long-term effectiveness and safety of the product are cited.

6. You are sure of the content of the product.

7. You have information that the manufacturer is reputable.

8. The known benefits are worth the cost.

9. There is evidence that you can get benefits from this product that cannot be obtained from good food.

10. There are no claims that use quack words or claims about conspiracies against the product by reputable organizations.

Food Supplement

Name: _____
_____
_____

Purported benefit: _____
_____
_____

Manufacturer/seller: _____
_____
_____

Dose and active ingredient: _____
_____
_____

Website

Web address: _____
_____
_____

Type of information provided: ____
_____
_____

Organization or person responsible for information: _____
_____
_____

Website

1. The site does not sell products associated with information provided.

2. The provider is a person, an organization (org), or a governmental agency (gov) with a sound reputation.

3. The site does not use quack words.

4. The site does not try to discredit well-established organizations or governmental agencies.

5. The site does not rely on testimonials, celebrities, or people with unknown credentials.

6. The site is well regarded by experts (e.g., check ratings on sites such as at http://navigator.tufts.edu).

7. The site has a history of providing good information.

8. The site provides complete information that is documented by research.

9. No claims of quick cures or miracle results are made.

10. The site provides information consistent with information provided in this text.

Conclusions and Implications

Total the number of Xs for the device, book/magazine, advertisement, food supplement, or website: _____

In several sentences, give your assessment of the product. Did it score well? Would you use/buy the product? Explain.

Lab 18B Evaluating a Health/Wellness or Fitness Club

Name	Section	Date

Purpose: To practice evaluating a health club (various combinations of the words *health, wellness,* and *fitness* are often used for these clubs)

Procedures

1. Choose a club and make a visit.
2. Listen carefully to all that is said and ask lots of questions.
3. Look carefully all around as you are given the tour of the facilities; ask what the exercises or the equipment does for you, or ask leading questions, such as, "Will this take inches off my hips?"
4. As soon as you leave the club, rate it, using Chart 1. Space is provided for notes in Chart 1.

Chart 1 Health Club Evaluation Questionnaire

Directions: Place an X over a "yes" or "no" answer. Make notes as necessary.

	Yes	No	Notes
1. Were claims for improvement in weight, figure/physique, or fitness realistic?	○	○	
2. Was a long-term contract (1 to 3 years) encouraged?	○	○	
3. Was the sales pitch high-pressure to make an immediate decision?	○	○	
4. Were you given a copy of the contract to read at home?	○	○	
5. Did the fine print include objectionable clauses?	○	○	
6. Did they ask you about medical readiness?	○	○	
7. Did they sell diet supplements as a sideline?	○	○	
8. Did they have passive equipment?	○	○	
9. Did they have cardiovascular training equipment or facilities (cycles, track, pool, aerobic dance)?	○	○	
10. Did they make unscientific claims for the equipment, exercise, baths, or diet supplements?	○	○	
11. Were the facilities clean?	○	○	
12. Were the facilities crowded?	○	○	
13. Were there days and hours when the facilities were open but would not be available to you?	○	○	
14. Were there limits on the number of minutes you could use a piece of equipment?	○	○	
15. Did the floor personnel closely supervise and assist clients?	○	○	
16. Were the floor personnel qualified experts?	○	○	
17. Were the managers/owners qualified experts?	○	○	
18. Has the club been in business at this location for a year or more?	○	○	

Results

1. Score the chart as follows:
    A. Give 1 point for each "no" answer for items 2, 3, 5, 7, 8, 10, 12, 13, and 14 and place the score in the box.

    Total A

    B. Give 1 point for each "yes" answer for items 1, 4, 6, 9, 11, and 18 and place the score in the box.

    Total B

    Total A and B above and place the score in the box.

    Total A and B

    C. Give 1 point for each "yes" answer for items 15, 16, and 17 and place the score in the box.

    Total C

2. A total score of 12–15 points on items A and B suggests the club rates at least fair, compared with other clubs.
3. A score of 3 on item C indicates that the personnel are qualified and suggests that you could expect to get accurate technical advice from the staff.
4. Regardless of the total scores, you would have to decide the importance of each item to you personally, as well as evaluate other considerations, such as cost, location, and personalities of the clients and the personnel, to decide if this would be a good place for you or your friends to join.

Conclusions and Implications: In several sentences, discuss your conclusion about the quality of this club and whether you think it would fit your needs if you wanted to belong.

Lab 19A Assessing Factors That Influence Health, Wellness, and Fitness

Name	Section	Date

Purpose: To assess the factors that relate to health, wellness, and fitness

Chart 1 Assessment Questionnaire: Factors That Influence Health, Wellness, and Fitness

Factor	Very True	Somewhat True	Not True At All	Score
Heredity				
1. I have checked my family history for medical problems.	③	②	①	
2. I have taken steps to overcome hereditary predispositions.	③	②	①	
			Heredity Score =	
Health Care				
3. I have health insurance.	③	②	①	
4. I get regular medical exams and have my own doctor.	③	②	①	
5. I get treatment early, rather than waiting until problems get serious	③	②	①	
6. I carefully investigate my health problems before making decisions.	③	②	①	
			Health-Care Score =	
Environment				
7. My physical environment is healthy.	③	②	①	
8. My social environment is healthy.	③	②	①	
9. My spiritual environment is healthy.	③	②	①	
10. My intellectual environment is healthy.	③	②	①	
11. My work environment is healthy.	③	②	①	
12. My environment fosters healthy lifestyles.	③	②	①	
			Environment Score =	
Lifestyles				
13. I am physically active on a regular basis.	③	②	①	
14. I eat well.	③	②	①	
15. I use effective techniques for managing stress.	③	②	①	
16. I avoid destructive behaviors.	③	②	①	
17. I practice safe sex.	③	②	①	
18. I manage my time effectively.	③	②	①	
19. I evaluate information carefully and am an informed consumer.	③	②	①	
20. My personal health habits are good.	③	②	①	
21. My safety habits are good.	③	②	①	
22. I know first aid and can use it if needed.	③	②	①	
			Lifestyles Score =	
Personal Actions and Interactions				
23. I collect and evaluate information before I act.	③	②	①	
24. I plan before I take action.	③	②	①	
25. I am good about taking action when I know it is good for me.	③	②	①	
26. I honor my beliefs and relationships.	③	②	①	
27. I seek help when I need it.	③	②	①	
			Personal Actions/Interactions Score =	

Procedures

1. Answer each of the questions in Chart 1 on page 433. Consider the information in this concept as you answer each question. The five factors assessed in the questionnaire are from Figure 1, page 424.
2. Calculate the scores for heredity (sum items 1 and 2), health care (sum items 3–6), environment (sum items 7–12), lifestyles (sum items 13–22), and actions/interactions (sum items 23–27).
3. Determine ratings for each of the scores using the Rating Chart.
4. Record your scores and ratings in the Results chart. Record your comments in the Conclusions and Implications section.

Results

Factor	Score	Rating
Heredity		
Health care		
Environment		
Lifestyles		
Actions/interactions		

Rating Chart

Factor	Healthy	Marginal	Needs Attention
Heredity	6	4–5	Below 4
Health care	11–12	9–10	Below 9
Environment	16–18	13–15	Below 13
Lifestyles	26–30	20–25	Below 20
Actions/interactions	13–15	10–12	Below 10

Conclusions and Implications

1. In the space below, discuss your scores for the five factors (sums of several questions) identified in Chart 1. Use several sentences to identify specific areas that need attention and changes that you could make to improve.

2. For any individual item on Chart 1, a score of 1 is considered low. You might have a high score on a set of questions and still have a low score in one area that indicates a need for attention. In several sentences, discuss actions you could take to make changes related to individual questions.

Lab 19B Planning for Improved Health, Wellness, and Fitness

Name	Section	Date

Purpose: To plan to make changes in areas that can most contribute to improved health, wellness, and fitness

Procedures

1. Experts agree that it is best not to make too many changes all at once. Focusing attention on one or two things at a time will produce better results. Based on your assessments made in Lab 19A, select two areas in which you would like to make changes. Choose one from the list related to health care and environment and one related to lifestyle change. Place a check by those areas in Chart 1 in the Results section. Because Lab 19C is devoted to physical activity, it is not included in the list. You may want to make additional copies of this lab for use in making other changes in the future.
2. Use Chart 2 to determine your Stage of Change for the changes you have identified. Since you have identified these as an area of need, it is unlikely that you would identify the stage of maintenance. If you are at maintenance, you can select a different area of change that would be more useful.
3. In the appropriate locations, record the change you want to make related to your environment or health care. State your reasons, your specific goal(s), your written statement of the plan for change, and a statement about how you will self-monitor and evaluate the effectiveness of the changes made. In Chart 3, record similar information for the lifestyle change you identified.

Results

Chart 1

Check one in each column.

Area of Change	✔	Area of Change	✔
Health insurance		Eating well	
Medical checkups		Managing stress	
Selecting a doctor		Avoiding destructive habits	
Physical environment		Practicing safe sex	
Social environment		Managing time	
Spiritual environment		Becoming a better consumer	
Intellectual environment		Improving health habits	
Work environment		Improving safety habits	
Environment for lifestyles		Learning first aid	

Chart 2

List the two areas of change identified in Chart 1. Make a rating using the diagram at the right.

Identified Area of Change	Stage of Change Rating
1.	
2.	

Maintenance — The change has lasted at least 6 months.

Action — "I have made some short-term changes."

Preparation — "I am getting ready to change."

Contemplation — "I am thinking about a change."

Precontemplation — "I don't want to change."

Note: Some of the areas identified in this lab relate to personal information. It is appropriate not to divulge personal information to others (including your instructor) if you choose not to. For this reason, you may choose not to address certain problems in this lab. You are encouraged to take steps to make changes independent of this assignment and to consult privately with your instructor to get assistance.

Lab 19B

Planning for Improved Health, Wellness, and Fitness

Chart 3 Making Changes for Improved Health, Wellness, and Fitness

Describe First Area of Change (from Chart 1)	Describe Second Area of Change (from Chart 1)
Step 1: State Reasons for Making Change	**Step 1: State Reasons for Making Change**
Step 2: Self-Assessment of Need for Change List your stage from Chart 2.	**Step 2: Self-Assessment of Need for Change** List your stage from Chart 2.
Step 3: State Your Specific Goals for Change State several specific and realistic goals.	**Step 3: State Your Specific Goals for Change** State several specific and realistic goals.
Step 4: Identify Activities or Actions for Change List specific activities you will do or actions you will take to meet your goals.	**Step 4: Identify Activities or Actions for Change** List specific activities you will do or actions you will take to meet your goals.

Step 5: Write a Plan; Include a Timetable
Expected start date:

Expected finish date:

Days of week and times: list times below days.

Mon.	Tue.	Wed.	Th.	Fri.	Sat.	Sun.

Location: Where will you do the plan?

Step 5: Write a Plan; Include a Timetable
Expected start date:

Expected finish date:

Days of week and times: list times below days.

Mon.	Tue.	Wed.	Th.	Fri.	Sat.	Sun.

Location: Where will you do the plan?

Step 6: Evaluate Your Plan
How will you self-monitor and evaluate to determine if the plan is working?

Step 6: Evaluate Your Plan
How will you self-monitor and evaluate to determine if the plan is working?

Lab 19C Planning Your Personal Physical Activity Program

Name	Section	Date

Purpose: To establish a comprehensive plan of lifestyle physical activity and to self-monitor progress in your plan (note: you may want to reread the concept on planning for physical activity before completing this lab)

Procedures

Step 1. Establishing Your Reasons

In the spaces provided below, list several of your principal reasons for doing a comprehensive activity plan.

1.

2.

3.

4.

5.

6.

Step 2. Identify Your Needs Using Fitness Self-Assessments and Ratings of Stage of Change for Various Activities

In Chart 1, rate your fitness by placing an X over the circle by the appropriate rating for each part of fitness. Use your results obtained from previous labs or perform the self-assessments again to determine your ratings. If you took more than one self-assessment for one component of physical fitness, select the rating that you think best describes your true fitness for that fitness component. If you were unable to do a self-assessment for some reason, check the "No Results" circle.

Chart 1 Rating for Self-Assessments

Health-Related Fitness Tests	Rating				
	High-Performance Zone	Good Fitness Zone	Marginal Zone	Low Zone	No Results
1. Cardiovascular: 12-minute run (Chart 6, page 133)	○	○	○	○	○
2. Cardiovascular: step test (Chart 2, page 131)	○	○	○	○	○
3. Cardiovascular: bicycle test (Chart 5, page 133)	○	○	○	○	○
4. Cardiovascular: walking test (Chart 1, page 131)	○	○	○	○	○
5. Cardiovascular: swim test (Chart 7, page 134)	○	○	○	○	○
6. Flexibility: sit-and-reach test (Chart 1, page 220)	○	○	○	○	○
7. Flexibility: shoulder flexibility (Chart 1, page 220)	○	○	○	○	○
8. Flexibility: hamstring/hip flexibility (Chart 1, page 220)	○	○	○	○	○
9. Flexibility: trunk rotation (Chart 1, page 220)	○	○	○	○	○
10. Strength: isometric grip (Chart 3, page 190)	○	○	○	○	○
11. Strength: 1 RM upper body (Chart 2, page 188)	○	○	○	○	○

Chart 1 Rating for Self-Assessments, *continued*

Health-Related Fitness Tests	Rating				
	High-Performance	Good Fitness	Marginal	Low	No Results
12. Strength: 1 RM lower body (Chart 2, page 188)	◯	◯	◯	◯	◯
13. Muscular endurance: curl-up (Chart 4, page 190)	◯	◯	◯	◯	◯
14. Muscular endurance: 90-degree push-up (Chart 4, page 190)	◯	◯	◯	◯	◯
15. Muscular endurance: flexed arm support (Chart 5, page 190)	◯	◯	◯	◯	◯
16. Fitness rating: skinfold (Chart 1, page 306)	◯	◯	◯	◯	◯
17. Body mass index (Chart 7, page 311)	◯	◯	◯	◯	◯

Skill-Related Fitness and Other Self-Assessments	Rating				
	Excellent	Very Good or Good	Fair	Poor	No Results
1. Agility (Chart 1, page 281)	◯	◯	◯	◯	◯
2. Balance (Chart 2, page 282)	◯	◯	◯	◯	◯
3. Coordination (Chart 3, page 282)	◯	◯	◯	◯	◯
4. Power (Chart 4, page 283)	◯	◯	◯	◯	◯
5. Reaction time (Chart 5, page 283)	◯	◯	◯	◯	◯
6. Speed (Chart 6, page 284)	◯	◯	◯	◯	◯
7. Fitness of the back (Chart 2, page 258)	◯	◯	◯	◯	◯
8. Posture (Chart 2, page 261)	◯	◯	◯	◯	◯

Summarize Your Fitness Ratings Using the Results Above	Rating				
	High-Performance	Good Fitness	Marginal	Low	No Results
Cardiovascular	◯	◯	◯	◯	◯
Flexibility	◯	◯	◯	◯	◯
Strength	◯	◯	◯	◯	◯
Muscular Endurance	◯	◯	◯	◯	◯
Body fatness	◯	◯	◯	◯	◯

	Excellent	Very Good or Good	Fair	Poor	No Results
Skill-related fitness	◯	◯	◯	◯	◯
Posture and fitness of the back	◯	◯	◯	◯	◯

Rate your stage of change for each of the different types of activities from the physical activity pyramid. Make an X over the circle beside the stage that best represents your behavior for each of the five types of activity in the lower three levels of the pyramid. A description of the various stages is provided below to help you make your ratings.

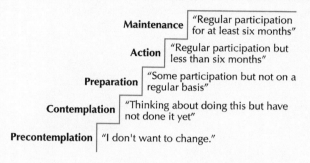

Maintenance "Regular participation for at least six months"

Action "Regular participation but less than six months"

Preparation "Some participation but not on a regular basis"

Contemplation "Thinking about doing this but have not done it yet"

Precontemplation "I don't want to change."

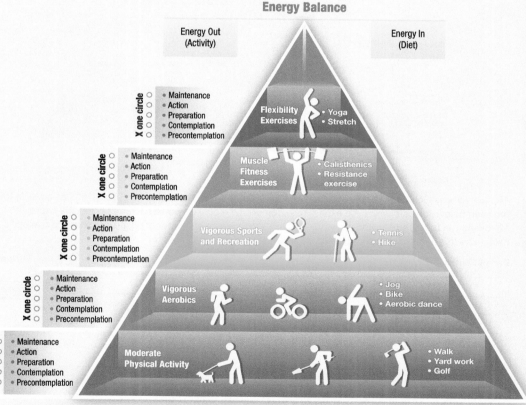

Energy Balance

Energy Out (Activity)

Energy In (Diet)

X one circle
- Maintenance
- Action
- Preparation
- Contemplation
- Precontemplation

Flexibility Exercises
- Yoga
- Stretch

X one circle
- Maintenance
- Action
- Preparation
- Contemplation
- Precontemplation

Muscle Fitness Exercises
- Calisthenics
- Resistance exercise

X one circle
- Maintenance
- Action
- Preparation
- Contemplation
- Precontemplation

Vigorous Sports and Recreation
- Tennis
- Hike

X one circle
- Maintenance
- Action
- Preparation
- Contemplation
- Precontemplation

Vigorous Aerobics
- Jog
- Bike
- Aerobic dance

X one circle
- Maintenance
- Action
- Preparation
- Contemplation
- Precontemplation

Moderate Physical Activity
- Walk
- Yard work
- Golf

*150 minutes of moderate or 75 minutes of vigorous activity per week is recommended; moderate and vigorous activity can be combined to meet guidelines.

Avoid Inactivity

Source: C. B. Corbin

In Step 1, you wrote down some general reasons for developing your physical activity plan. Setting goals requires more specific statements of goals that are realistic and achievable. For people who are at the contemplation or preparation stage for a specific type of activity, it is recommended that you write only short-term physical activity goals (no more than 4 weeks). Those at the action or maintenance level may choose short-term goals to start with, or if you have a good history of adherence, choose long-term goals (longer than 4 weeks). Precontemplators are not considered because they would not be doing this activity.

Step 3. Set Specific Goals

Chart 2 Setting Goals

Physical Activity Goals. Place an X over the appropriate circle for the number of days and weeks for each type of activity. Write the number of exercises or minutes of activities you plan in each of the five areas.

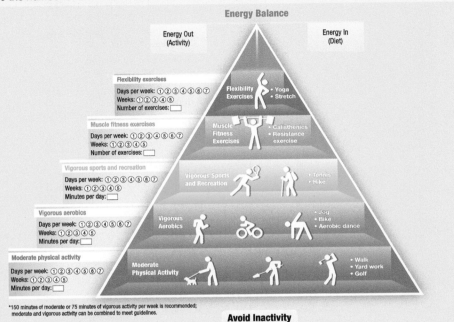

Energy Balance

Energy Out (Activity)   Energy In (Diet)

Flexibility exercises
Days per week: ① ② ③ ④ ⑤ ⑥ ⑦
Weeks: ① ② ③ ④ ⑤
Number of exercises: ☐

Muscle fitness exercises
Days per week: ① ② ③ ④ ⑤ ⑥ ⑦
Weeks: ① ② ③ ④ ⑤
Number of exercises: ☐

Vigorous sports and recreation
Days per week: ① ② ③ ④ ⑤ ⑥ ⑦
Weeks: ① ② ③ ④ ⑤
Minutes per day: ☐

Vigorous aerobics
Days per week: ① ② ③ ④ ⑤ ⑥ ⑦
Weeks: ① ② ③ ④ ⑤
Minutes per day: ☐

Moderate physical activity
Days per week: ① ② ③ ④ ⑤ ⑥ ⑦
Weeks: ① ② ③ ④ ⑤
Minutes per day: ☐

Flexibility Exercises • Yoga • Stretch

Muscle Fitness Exercises • Calisthenics • Resistance exercise

Vigorous Sports and Recreation • Tennis • Hike

Vigorous Aerobics • Jog • Bike • Aerobic dance

Moderate Physical Activity • Walk • Yard work • Golf

*150 minutes of moderate or 75 minutes of vigorous activity per week is recommended; moderate and vigorous activity can be combined to meet guidelines.

Avoid Inactivity

Source: C. B. Corbin

Physical Fitness Goals (for People at Action or Maintenance Only). Write specific physical fitness goals in the spaces provided below. Indicate when you expect to accomplish the goal (in weeks). Examples include improving the 12-minute run to a specific score, being able to perform a specific number of push-ups, attaining a specific BMI, and being able to achieve a specific score on a flexibility test.

Part of Fitness	Description of Specific Performance	Weeks to Goal

Step 4. Selecting Activities

In Chart 3, indicate the specific activities you plan to perform from each area of the physical activity pyramid. If the activity you expect to perform is listed, note the number of minutes or reps/sets you plan to perform. If the activity you want to perform is not listed, write the name of the activity or exercise in the space designated as "Other." For lifestyle activities, active aerobics, and active sports and recreation, indicate the length of time the activity will be performed each day. For flexibility, muscle fitness exercises, and exercises for back and neck, indicate the number of repetitions for each exercise.

Chart 3 Lifetime Physical Activity Selections

✔	Lifestyle Activities	Min./Day	✔	Active Aerobics	Min./Day	✔	Active Sports and Recreation	Min./Day
	Walking			Aerobic exercise machines			Basketball	
	Yard work			Bicycling			Bowling	
	Active housework			Circuit training or calisthenics			Golf	
	Gardening			Dance or step aerobics			Karate/judo	
	Social dancing			Hiking or backpacking			Mountain climbing	
	Occupational activity			Jogging or running (or walking)			Racquetball	
	Wheeling in wheelchair			Skating/cross-country skiing			Skating	
	Bicycling to work or store			Swimming			Softball	
	Other:			Water activity			Skiing	
	Other:			Other:			Soccer	
	Other:			Other:			Volleyball	
	Other:			Other:			Other:	
	Other:			Other:			Other:	
	Other:			Other:			Other:	
	Other:			Other:			Other:	

✔	Flexibility Exercises	Reps/Sets	✔	Muscle Fitness Exercises	Reps/Sets	✔	Exercises for Back and Neck	Reps/Sets
	Calf stretch			Bench or seated press			Back saver stretch	
	Hip and thigh stretch			Biceps curl			Single knee to chest	
	Sitting stretch			Triceps curl			Low back stretch	
	Hamstring stretch			Lat pull down			Hip/thigh stretch	
	Back stretch (leg hug)			Seated rowing			Pelvic tilt	
	Trunk twist			Wrist curl			Bridging	
	Pectoral stretch			Knee extension			Wall slide	
	Arm stretch			Heel raise			Pelvic stabilizer	
	Other:			Half-squat skiing			Neck rotation	
	Other:			Lunge			Isometric neck exercise	
	Other:			Toe press			Chin tuck	
	Other:			Crunch or reverse curl			Trapezius stretch	
	Other:			Other:			Other:	
	Other:			Other:			Other:	
	Other:			Other:			Other:	

Lab 19C

Planning Your Personal Physical Activity Program

Planning Your Personal Physical Activity Program

Step 5. Preparing a Written Plan

In Chart 4, place a check in the shaded boxes for each activity you will perform for each day you will do it. Indicate the time of day you expect to perform the activity or exercise (Example: 7:30 to 8 A.M. or 6 to 6:30 P.M.). In the spaces labeled "Warm-Up Exercises" and "Cool-Down Exercises," check the warm-up and cool-down exercises you expect to perform. Indicate the number of reps you will use for each exercise.

Chart 4 My Physical Activity Plan

✔	Monday	Time	✔	Tuesday	Time	✔	Wednesday	Time
	Lifestyle activity			Lifestyle activity			Lifestyle activity	
	Active aerobics			Active aerobics			Active aerobics	
	Active sports/rec.			Active sports/rec.			Active sports/rec.	
	Flexibility exercises*			Flexibility exercises*			Flexibility exercises*	
	Muscle fitness exercises*			Muscle fitness exercises*			Muscle fitness exercises*	
	Back/neck exercises*			Back/neck exercises*			Back/neck exercises*	
	Warm-up exercises			Warm-up exercises			Warm-up exercises	
	Other:			Other:			Other:	

✔	Thursday	Time	✔	Friday	Time	✔	Saturday	Time
	Lifestyle activity			Lifestyle activity			Lifestyle activity	
	Active aerobics			Active aerobics			Active aerobics	
	Active sports/rec.			Active sports/rec.			Active sports/rec.	
	Flexibility exercises*			Flexibility exercises*			Flexibility exercises*	
	Muscle fitness exercises*			Muscle fitness exercises*			Muscle fitness exercises*	
	Back/neck exercises*			Back/neck exercises*			Back/neck exercises*	
	Warm-up exercises			Warm-up exercises			Warm-up exercises	
	Other:			Other:			Other:	

✔	Sunday	Time	✔	Warm-Up Exercises	Reps	✔	Cool-Down Exercises	Reps
	Lifestyle activity			Walk or jog 1–2 min.			Walk or jog 1–2 min.	
	Active aerobics			Calf stretch			Calf stretch	
	Active sports/rec.			Hamstring stretch			Hamstring stretch	
	Flexibility exercises*			Leg hug			Leg hug	
	Muscle fitness exercises*			Sitting side stretch			Sitting side stretch	
	Back/neck exercises*			Zipper			Zipper	
	Warm-up exercises			Other:			Other:	
	Other:			Other:			Other:	

*Perform the specific exercises you checked in Chart 3.

Step 6. Keeping Records of Progress and Evaluating Your Plan

Make copies of Chart 4 (one for each week that you plan to keep records). Each day, make a check by the activities you actually performed. Include the times when you actually did the activities in your plan. Periodically check your goals to see if they have been accomplished. At some point, it will be necessary to reestablish your goals and create a revised activity plan.

Results

After performing your plan for a specific period of time, answer the question in the space provided.

How long have you been performing the plan? [   ]

Conclusions and Implications

1. In several sentences, discuss your adherence to the plan. Have you been able to stick with the plan? If so, do you think it is a plan you can do for a lifetime? If not, why do you think you are unable to do your plan?

2. In several sentences, discuss how you might modify your plan in the future.

3. In several sentences, discuss your goals for your program. Do you think you will meet your goals? Why or why not?

Appendix A
Metric Conversion Charts

Chart 1 Traditional/Metric Measurement Conversions

	Metrics to Traditional	Traditional to Metrics
Length	centimeters to inches: cm × .39 = 1 in.	inches to centimeters: in. × 2.54 = cm
	meters to feet: m × 3.3 = ft.	feet to meters: ft. × .3048 = m
	meters to yards: m × 1.09 = yd.	yards to meters: yd. × 0.92 = m
	kilometers to miles: km × 0.6 = mi.	miles to kilometers: mi. × 1.6 = km
Weight (Mass)	grams to ounces: g × 0.0352 = oz.	ounces to grams: oz. × 28.41 = g
	kilograms to pounds: kg × 2.2 = lb.	pounds to kilograms: lb. × 0.45 = kg
Volume	milliliters to fluid ounces: ml × 0.03 = fl. oz.	fluid ounces to milliliters: fl. oz. × 29.573 = ml
	liters to quarts: l × 1.06 = qt.	quarts to liters: qt. × 0.95 = l
	liters to gallons: l × 0.264 = gal.	gallons to liters: gal. × 3.8 = l

Chart 2 Isometric Strength Rating Scale (kg)—page 190

	Men			Women		
Classification	Left Grip	Right Grip	Total Score	Left Grip	Right Grip	Total Score
High-performance zone	57+	61+	118+	34+	39+	73+
Good fitness zone	45–56	50–60	95–117	27–33	32–38	59–72
Marginal zone	41–44	43–49	84–94	20–26	23–31	43–58
Low zone	<41	<43	<84	<20	<23	<43

Suitable for use by young adults between 18 and 30 years of age. After 30, an adjustment of 0.5 of 1 percent per year is appropriate because some loss of muscle tissue typically occurs as you grow older.

Chart 3 Power Rating Scale—page 283

Classification	Men	Women
Excellent	68 cm+	60 cm+
Very good	53–67 cm	48–59 cm
Good	42–52 cm	37–47 cm
Fair	31–41 cm	27–36 cm
Poor	<32 cm	<27 cm

Chart 4 Reaction Time Rating Scale—page 283

Classification	Score in Inches	Score in Centimeters
Excellent	>21	>52
Very good	19″–21	48–52
Good	16″–18 ¾	41–47
Fair	13″–15 ¾	33–40
Poor	<13	<33

Chart 5 Speed Rating Scale—page 284

	Men		Women	
Classification	Yards	Meters	Yards	Meters
Excellent	24+	22+	22+	20+
Very good	22–23	20–21.9	20–21	18–19.9
Good	18–21	16.5–19.9	16–19	14.5–17.9
Fair	16–17	14.5–16.4	14–15	13–14.4
Poor	<16	<14.5	<14	<13

Appendix B
Canada's Food Guide to Healthy Eating

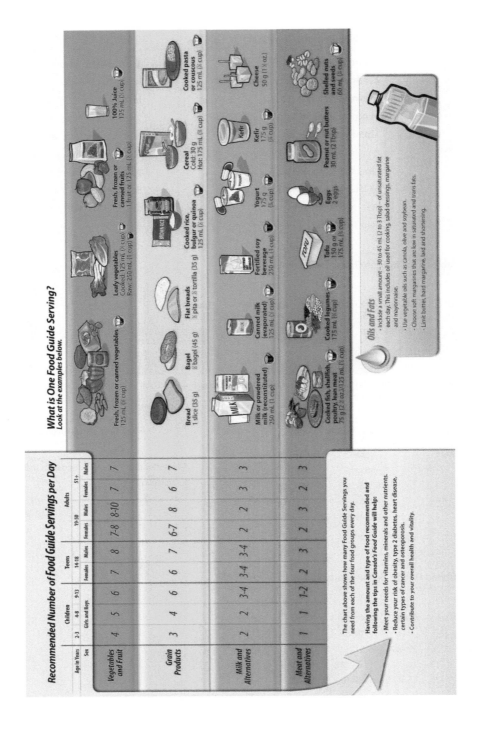

Make each Food Guide Serving count...
wherever you are – at home, at school, at work or when eating out!

▶ **Eat at least one dark green and one orange vegetable each day.**
- Go for dark green vegetables such as broccoli, romaine lettuce and spinach.
- Go for orange vegetables such as carrots, sweet potatoes and winter squash.

▶ **Choose vegetables and fruit prepared with little or no added fat, sugar or salt.**
- Enjoy vegetables steamed, baked or stir-fried instead of deep-fried.

▶ **Have vegetables and fruit more often than juice.**

▶ **Make at least half of your grain products whole grain each day.**
- Eat a variety of whole grains such as barley, brown rice, oats, quinoa and wild rice.
- Enjoy whole grain breads, oatmeal or whole wheat pasta.

▶ **Choose grain products that are lower in fat, sugar or salt.**
- Compare the Nutrition Facts table on labels to make wise choices.
- Enjoy the true taste of grain products. When adding sauces or spreads, use small amounts.

▶ **Drink skim, 1%, or 2% milk each day.**
- Have 500 mL (2 cups) of milk every day for adequate vitamin D.
- Drink fortified soy beverages if you do not drink milk.

▶ **Select lower fat milk alternatives.**
- Compare the Nutrition Facts table on yogurts or cheeses to make wise choices.

▶ **Have meat alternatives such as beans, lentils and tofu often.**

▶ **Eat at least two Food Guide Servings of fish each week.***
- Choose fish such as char, herring, mackerel, salmon, sardines and trout.

▶ **Select lean meat and alternatives prepared with little or no added fat or salt.**
- Trim the visible fat from meats. Remove the skin on poultry.
- Use cooking methods such as roasting, baking or poaching that require little or no added fat.
- If you eat luncheon meats, sausages or prepackaged meats, choose those lower in salt (sodium) and fat.

Enjoy a variety of foods from the four food groups.

Satisfy your thirst with water!

Drink water regularly. It's a calorie-free way to quench your thirst. Drink more water in hot weather or when you are very active.

* Health Canada provides advice for limiting exposure to mercury from certain types of fish. Refer to www.healthcanada.gc.ca for the latest information.

Appendix C
Calories of Protein, Carbohydrates, and Fats in Foods

Food Choice	Total Calories	Protein Calories	Carbohydrate Calories	Fat Calories
Breakfast				
Scrambled egg (1 lg.)	111	29	7	75
Fried egg (1 lg.)	99	26	1	72
Pancake (1-6)	146	19	67	58
Syrup (1 T[4])	60	0	60	0
French toast (1 slice)	180	23	49	108
Waffle (7-inch)	245	28	100	117
Biscuit (medium)	104	8	52	44
Bran muffin (medium)	104	11	63	31
White toast (slice)	68	9	52	7
Wheat toast (slice)	67	14	52	6
Peanut butter (1 T)	94	15	11	68
Yogurt (8 oz. plain)	227	39	161	27
Orange juice (8 oz.)	114	8	100	6
Apple juice (8 oz.)	117	1	116	0
Soft drink (12 oz.)	144	0	144	0
Bacon (2 slices)	86	15	2	70
Sausage (1 link)	141	11	0	130
Sausage (1 patty)	284	23	0	261
Grits (8 oz.)	125	11	110	4
Hash browns (8 oz.)	355	18	178	159
French fries (reg.)	239	12	115	112
Donut, cake	125	4	61	60
Donut, glazed	164	8	87	69
Sweet roll	317	22	136	159
Cake (medium slice)	274	14	175	85
Ice cream (8 oz.)	257	15	108	134
Cream cheese (T)	52	4	1	47
Jelly (T)	49	0	49	0
Jam (T)	54	0	54	0
Coffee (cup)	0	0	0	0
Tea (cup)	0	0	0	0
Cream (T)	32	2	2	28
Sugar (t)	15	0	15	0
Corn flakes (8 oz.)	97	8	87	2
Wheat flakes (8 oz.)	106	12	90	4
Oatmeal (8 oz.)	132	19	92	21
Strawberries (8 oz.)	55	4	46	5
Orange (medium)	64	6	57	1
Apple (medium)	96	1	86	9
Banana (medium)	101	4	95	2
Cantaloupe (half)	82	7	73	2
Grapefruit (half)	40	2	37	1
Custard pie (slice)	285	20	188	77
Fruit pie (slice)	350	14	259	77
Fritter (medium)	132	11	54	67
Skim milk (8 oz.)	88	36	52	0

Food Choice	Total Calories	Protein Calories	Carbohydrate Calories	Fat Calories
Whole milk (8 oz.)	159	33	48	78
Butter (pat)	36	0	0	36
Margarine (pat)	36	0	0	36
Lunch				
Hamburger (reg. FF[1])	255	48	120	89
Cheeseburger (reg. FF)	307	61	120	126
Doubleburger (FF)	563	101	163	299
¼ lb. burger (FF)	427	73	137	217
Doublecheese burger (FF)	670	174	134	362
Doublecheese baconburger (FF)	724	138	174	340
Hot dog (FF)	214	36	54	124
Chili dog (FF)	320	51	90	179
Pizza, cheese (slice FF)	290	116	116	58
Pizza, meat (slice FF)	360	126	126	108
Pizza, everything (slice FF)	510	179	173	158
Sandwich, roast beef (FF)	350	88	126	137
Sandwich, bologna	313	44	106	163
Sandwich, bologna-cheese	428	69	158	201
Sandwich, ham-cheese (FF)	380	91	133	156
Sandwich, peanut butter	281	39	118	124
Sandwich, PB and jelly	330	40	168	122
Sandwich, egg salad	330	40	109	181
Sandwich, tuna salad	390	101	109	180
Sandwich, fish (FF)	432	56	147	229
French fries (reg. FF)	239	12	115	112
French fries (lg. FF)	406	20	195	191
Onion rings (reg. FF)	274	14	112	148
Chili (8 oz.)	260	49	62	148
Bean soup (8 oz.)	355	67	181	107
Beef noodle soup (8 oz.)	140	32	59	49
Tomato soup (8 oz.)	180	14	121	45
Vegetable soup (8 oz.)	160	21	107	32
Small salad, plain	37	6	27	4
Small salad, French dressing	152	8	50	94
Small salad, Italian dressing	162	8	28	126
Small salad, bleu cheese	184	13	28	143
Potato salad (8 oz.)	248	27	159	62
Cole slaw (8 oz.)	180	0	25	155
Macaroni and cheese (8 oz.)	230	37	103	90
Beef taco (FF)	186	59	56	71
Bean burrito (FF)	343	45	192	106
Meat burrito (FF)	466	158	196	112
Mexican rice (FF)	213	17	160	36
Mexican beans (FF)	168	42	82	44
Fried chicken breast (FF)	436	262	13	161
Broiled chicken breast	284	224	0	60

The principal reference for the calculation of values used in this appendix was the *Nutritive Value of Foods*, published by the United States Department of Agriculture, Washington, DC, Home and Gardens Bulletin, No. 72, although other published sources were consulted, including Jacobson, M., and S. Fritschner. *The Fast-Food Guide* (an excellent source of information about fast foods). New York: Workman.

Notes:
1. FF by a food indicates that it is typical of a food served in a fast food restaurant.
2. Your portions of foods may be larger or smaller than those listed here. For this reason, you may wish to select a food more than once (e.g., two hamburgers) or select only a portion of a serving (i.e., divide the calories in half for a half portion).
3. An oz. equals 28.35 grams.
4. T = tablespoon and t = teaspoon.

Appendix C   449

Food Choice	Total Calories	Protein Calories	Carbohydrate Calories	Fat Calories
Broiled fish	228	82	32	114
Fish stick (1 stick FF)	50	18	8	24
Fried egg	99	26	1	72
Donut	125	4	61	60
Potato chips (small bag)	115	3	39	73
Soft drink (12 oz.)	144	0	144	0
Apple juice (8 oz.)	117	1	116	0
Skim milk (8 oz.)	88	36	52	0
Whole milk (8 oz.)	159	33	48	78
Diet drink (12 oz.)	0	0	0	0
Mustard (t)	4	0	4	0
Catsup (t)	6	0	6	0
Mayonnaise (T)	100	0	0	100
Fruit pie	350	14	259	77
Cheesecake (slice)	400	56	132	212
Ice cream (8 oz.)	257	15	108	134
Coffee (8 oz.)	0	0	0	0
Tea (8 oz.)	0	0	0	0

Dinner

Food Choice	Total Calories	Protein Calories	Carbohydrate Calories	Fat Calories
Hamburger (reg. FF)	255	48	120	89
Cheeseburger (reg. FF)	307	61	120	126
Doubleburger (FF)	563	101	163	299
¼ lb. burger (FF)	427	73	137	217
Doublecheese burger (FF)	670	174	134	362
Doublecheese baconburger (FF)	724	138	174	412
Hot dog (FF)	214	36	54	124
Chili dog (FF)	320	51	90	179
Pizza, cheese (slice FF)	290	116	116	58
Pizza, meat (slice FF)	360	126	126	108
Pizza, everything (slice FF)	510	179	173	158
Steak (8 oz.)	880	290	0	590
French fried shrimp (6 oz.)	360	133	68	158
Roast beef (8 oz.)	440	268	0	172
Liver (8 oz.)	520	250	52	218
Corned beef (8 oz.)	493	242	0	251
Meat loaf (8 oz.)	711	228	35	448
Ham (8 oz.)	540	178	0	362
Spaghetti, no meat (13 oz.)	400	56	220	124
Spaghetti, meat (13 oz.)	500	115	230	155
Baked potato (medium)	90	12	78	0
Cooked carrots (8 oz.)	71	12	59	0
Cooked spinach (8 oz.)	50	18	18	14
Corn (1 ear)	70	10	52	8
Cooked green beans (8 oz.)	54	11	43	0
Cooked broccoli (8 oz.)	60	19	26	15
Cooked cabbage	47	12	35	0
French fries (reg. FF)	239	12	115	112
French fries (lg. FF)	406	20	195	191
Onion rings (reg. FF)	274	14	112	148
Chili (8 oz.)	260	49	62	148
Small salad, plain	37	6	27	4
Small salad, French dressing	152	8	50	94
Small salad, Italian dressing	162	8	28	126
Small salad, bleu cheese	184	13	28	143
Potato salad (8 oz.)	248	27	159	62
Cole slaw (8 oz.)	180	0	25	155
Macaroni and cheese (8 oz.)	230	37	103	90
Beef Taco (FF)	186	59	56	71
Bean burrito (FF)	343	45	192	106
Meat burrito (FF)	466	158	196	112

Food Choice	Total Calories	Protein Calories	Carbohydrate Calories	Fat Calories
Mexican rice (FF)	213	17	160	36
Mexican beans (FF)	168	42	82	44
Fried chicken breast (FF)	436	262	13	161
Broiled chicken breast	284	224	0	60
Broiled fish	228	82	32	114
Fish stick (1 stick FF)	50	18	8	24
Soft drink (12 oz.)	144	0	144	0
Apple juice (8 oz.)	117	1	116	0
Skim milk (8 oz.)	88	36	52	0
Whole milk (8 oz.)	159	33	48	78
Diet drink (12 oz.)	0	0	0	0
Mustard (t)	4	0	4	0
Catsup (t)	6	0	6	0
Mayonnaise (T)	100	0	0	100
Fruit pie (slice)	350	14	259	77
Cheesecake (slice)	400	56	132	212
Ice cream (8 oz.)	257	15	108	134
Custard pie (slice)	285	20	188	77
Cake (slice)	274	14	175	85

Snacks

Food Choice	Total Calories	Protein Calories	Carbohydrate Calories	Fat Calories
Peanut butter (1 T)	94	15	11	68
Yogurt (8 oz. plain)	227	39	161	27
Orange juice (8 oz.)	114	8	100	6
Apple juice (8 oz.)	117	1	116	0
Soft drink (12 oz.)	144	0	144	0
Donut, cake	125	4	61	60
Donut, glazed	164	8	87	69
Sweet roll	317	22	136	159
Cake (medium slice)	274	14	175	85
Ice cream (8 oz.)	257	15	108	134
Softserve cone (reg.)	240	10	89	134
Ice cream sandwich bar	210	40	82	88
Strawberries (8 oz.)	55	4	46	5
Orange (medium)	64	6	57	1
Apple (medium)	96	1	86	9
Banana (medium)	101	4	95	2
Cantaloupe (half)	82	7	73	2
Grapefruit (half)	40	2	37	1
Celery stick	5	2	3	0
Carrot (medium)	20	3	17	0
Raisins (4 oz.)	210	6	204	0
Watermelon (4" × 6" slice)	115	8	99	8
Chocolate chip cookie	60	3	9	48
Brownie	145	6	26	113
Oatmeal cookie	65	3	13	49
Sandwich cookie	200	8	112	80
Custard pie (slice)	285	20	188	77
Fruit pie (slice)	350	14	259	77
Gelatin (4 oz.)	70	4	32	34
Fritter (medium)	132	11	54	67
Skim milk (8 oz.)	88	36	52	0
Diet drink	0	0	0	0
Potato chips (small bag)	115	3	39	73
Roasted peanuts (1.3 oz.)	210	34	25	151
Chocolate candy bar (1 oz.)	145	7	61	77
Choc. almond candy bar (1 oz.)	265	38	74	164
Saltine cracker	18	1	1	16
Popped corn	40	7	33	0
Cheese nachos	471	63	194	214

Credits

Text Credits

2: *Healthy People 2020.* www.healthypeople.gov/
HP2020. 4: Trust for America's Health. 2008.
Blueprint for a Healthier America. Washington, DC:
Trust for America's Health. http://healthyamericans
.org/report/55/blueprint-for-healthier-america.
12: Institute of Medicine. 2004. *Insuring
America's Health: Principles and Recommendations.*
Washington, DC: The National Academies Press.
15: Mokdad, A. H. et al. 2004. Actual causes of
death in the United States, 2000. *Journal of the
American Medical Association* 291(10):1238–1245.
25: Buettner, D. 2008. *The Blue Zones: Lessons for
Living Longer from People Who've Lived the Longest.*
Washington, DC: The National Geographic Soci-
ety. 26: Christakis, N. A., and J. H. Fowler. 2007.
The spread of obesity in a large social network
over 32 years. *New England Journal of Medicine*
375(4):370–379. 44: ACSM. 2010. *ACSM's Guidelines for Exercise Testing and Prescription.* 8th ed.
Philadelphia: Lippincott, Williams & Wilkins.
44: United States Department of Health and
Human Services. 1996. *Physical Activity and Health:
A Report of the Surgeon General.* Washington, DC:
USDHHS. http://www.cdc.gov/nccdphp/sgr/index
.htm. 65: Health Canada. 1986. *Achieving Health
for All: A Framework for Health.* 65: USDHHS.
2008. *Physical Activity Guidelines for Americans.*
Atlanta, GA: Author. http://www.health.gov/
paguidelines. 69: National Cholesterol Education
Program. 2001. *Third Report of the National Cholesterol Education Program.* Atlanta, GA: National
Institutes of Health. Publication No. 02-5215.
www.nhlbi.nih.gov/guidelines/cholesterol/atp-
3full.pdf. 71: National Heart Lung and Blood
Institute. 2012. *What Is High Blood Pressure?*
http://www.nhlbi.nih.gov/health/health-topics/
topics/hbp. 73: National Cholesterol Education
Program. 2012. *Framingham Risk Assessment Tool.*
http://hp2010.nhlbihin.net/atpiii/calculator.asp.
75: National Center for Health Statistics. 2012.
Obesity and Overweight. www.cdc.gov/nchs/fastats/
overwt.htm. 78: Kennedy, J. F. 1960. The soft
American. *Sports Illustrated* 13(26):14–23. 90: Blair,
S. N. 2009. Physical inactivity: The biggest
public health problem of the 21st century.
British Journal of Sports Medicine 43(1):1–2.
90: Corbin, C. B. 2012. *The Physical Activity
Pyramid.* Used by permission. The source is the
same for all subsequent uses of the pyramid.

93: Centers for Disease Control and Prevention.
2007. Prevalence of regular physical activity
among adults—United States. *Morbidity and
Mortality Weekly Reports* 56(46):1209–1212.
93: Barnes, P. M., et al. 2009. Early release of
selected estimates based on data from the January–
June 2009 National Health Interview Survey.
National Center for Health Statistics. www.cdc
.gov/nchs/nhis/released200912.htm. 105: Levine,
J. A. 2007. Nonexercise activity thermogenesis—
Liberating the life-force. *Journal of Internal
Medicine* 263(3):273–287. 108: Ainsworth, B. E.
2000. Compendium of physical activities: An
update of activity codes and MET intensities.
Medicine and Science in Sports and Exercise 32
(Suppl):S498–S516. 110: National Association of
Realtor. 2011. *The 2011 Community Preference Survey.*
http://www.stablecommunities.org/sites/all/files/
library/1608/smartgrowthcommsurveyresults2011
.pdf. 121: Blair, S. N., et al. 1989. Physical
fitness and all-cause mortality. A prospective
study of healthy men and women. *Journal of
the American Medical Association* 363(17):2395–
2401. 125: Timmons, J. A., et al. 2010. Using
molecular classification to predict gains in maximal aerobic capacity following endurance exercise
training in humans. *Journal of Applied Physiology*
108(6):1487–1496. 127, 135: Borg, G. 1982.
Psychophysical bases of perceived exertion.
Medicine and Science in Sports and Exercise
14 (5):377–381. 147: Knab, A. M., et al. 2011.
45-minute vigorous exercise bout increases metabolic rate for 14 hours. *Medicine and Science in
Sports and Exercise* 43(9):1643–1648. 149: Sporting Goods Manufacturers Association. www.sgma
.com. 150: Sporting Goods Manufacturers Association. www.sgma.com. 158: Compendium
of Physical Activities. http://prevention.sph
.sc.edu/tools/docs/documents_compendium.pdf.
162: Williams, M. A., et al. 2007. Resistance exercise in individuals with and without cardiovascular
disease. 2007 update: A scientific statement from
the American Heart Association Council on Clinical Cardiology and Council on Nutrition, Physical
Activity, and Metabolism. *Circulation* 116(5):572–
584. 163: Growing Stronger: Strength Training
for Older Adults. www.cdc.gov/physicalactivity/
growingstronger/index.html. 165: Technogym,
www.technogym.com. 167: CrossFit Games,
http://games.crossfit.com. 175: P90X, www
.beachbody.com/P90X. 203: Pereles, D., A. Roth,

and D. J. S. Thompson. 2010. A large, randomized,
prospective study of the impact of a pre-run
stretch on the risk of injury in teenage and older
runners. *USA Track and Field.* http://www.usatf
.org/stretchStudy/StretchStudyReport.pdf.
210: Thompson, W. R. 2011. Worldwide survey of
fitness trends for 2012. *ACSM's Health and Fitness
Journal* 15(6):9–18. 210: FICSIT. www.ncbi.nlm
.nih.gov/pubmed/8617895. 270: Gibala, M. 2012.
Active voice: Is high-intensity interval training a
time-efficient exercise strategy to promote health?
Sports Medicine Bulletin, February 28. 273: Brit-
tenham, G. 1992. Plyometric exercise. A word of
caution. *Journal of Physical Education, Recreation and
Dance* 63(1):20–23. 281: Adams, W., et al. 1965.
Foundations of Physical Activity. Champaign, IL:
Stipes and Co. 291: World Health Organization.
BMI Classification. http://apps.who.int/bmi/
index.jsp?introPage=intro_3.html. 295: Wang, Y.,
et al. 2008. Will all Americans become overweight
or obese? Estimating the progression and cost of
the U.S. obesity epidemic. *Obesity* 16(10):2323–
2330. 295: Lee, C. D., A. S. Jackson, and S. N.
Blair. 1998. US Weight Guidelines: It is also
important to consider cardiorespiratory fitness.
International Journal of Obesity 22(supplement 2):S2.
305: Welk, G. J., and S. N. Blair. 2008. Health
benefits of physical activity and fitness in
children. In G. J. Welk and M. D. Meredith (Eds.),
Fitnessgram/Activitygram Reference Guide. Dallas,
TX: The Cooper Institute. http://www.cooper
institute.org/reference-guide. 308: Baumgartner,
T. A., and A. S. Jackson. 1999. *Measurement for
Evaluation in Physical Education and Exercise Science.*
Dubuque, IA: W. C. Brown Publishers. 310: Metropolitan Life Insurance Company. www.metlife
.com. 310: U. S. Department of Agriculture, www
.usda.gov, and Department of Health and Human
Services. www.hhs.gov. 324: USDA 2010. www
.choosemyplate.gov. 328: American Heart Association 2009. *AHA Scientific Statement: Dietary
Sugars Intake and Cardiovascular Health.* http://
circ.ahajournals.org/content/120/11/1011
.abstract. 328: American Dietetics Association.
2008. www.eatright.org/About/Content.aspx?
id=8355&terms=fiber. 328: International
Agency of Research on Cancer. www.iarc.fr.
331: Williams, M. H. 2001. *Nutrition for Health,
Fitness, and Sports.* 6th ed. St. Louis: McGraw-Hill.
334: Manore, M. M. 2001. Vitamins and minerals:
Part II. Who needs supplements? *ACSM's Health*

and Fitness Journal 5(3):30–34. **336:** U.S. Food and Drug Administration. www.fda.gov. **339:** Harris Interactive. 2011. Healthy eating habits differ the most between the old and the young. www.harrisinteractive.com/NewsRoom/HarrisPolls/tabid/447/mid/1508/articleId/762/ctl/ReadCustom%20Default/Default.aspx. **351:** International Food Information Council. 2012. *2012 Food & Health Survey: Consumer Attitudes toward Food Safety, Nutrition and Health.* www.foodinsight.org. **354:** Wansink, B. 2007. *Mindless Eating: Why We Eat More Than We Think.* New York: Bantam Books. **355:** American College of Sports Medicine. www.acsm.org/about-acsm/media-room/acsm-in-the-news/2011/08/01/acsm-position-stand-on-physical-activity-and-weight-loss-now-available. **356:** BodyMedia Fit. www.bodymedia.com. **358:** Northern Manhattan Study. 2011. Diet soda may raise odds of vascular events; salt linked to stroke risk. http://newsroom.heart.org/pr/aha/1249.aspx. **368:** Kanner, A. D., et al. 1981. Comparison of two modes of stress measurement: Daily hassles and uplifts versus major life events. *Journal of Behavioral Medicine* 4:1–39. **369:** American Psychological Association, 2012. *Stress In America,* www.apa.org/news/press/releases/stress/index.aspx. **370:** Gallagher, R. P. 2011. National Survey of Counseling Center Directors 2011. The International Association of Counseling Services, Inc. Monograph Series Number 8T. www.iacsinc.org/2011%20NSCCD.pdf. **370:** Gallup-Wellbeing Poll. www.gallup.com/poll/wellbeing.aspx. **371:** Selye, H. 1956. *The Stress of Life.* New York: McGraw-Hill. **373:** Thomas, J. L., et al. 2010. Prevalence of mental health problems and functional impairment among active component National Guard soldiers 3 and 12 months following combat in Iraq. *Archives of General Psychiatry* 67:614–623. **380:** Sarason, I. G., J. H. Johnson, and J. M. Siegel. 1978. Assessing the impact of life changes: Development of the life experiences survey. *Journal of Consulting and Clinical Psychology* 46(5):932–946. **386–387:** American Time Use Survey from the Bureau of Labor Statistics. www.bls.gov/tus. **387:** Mancini, M. 2003. *Time Management.* McGraw-Hill: Blacklick, OH. **390:** Burns, D. D. 1999. *The Feeling Good Handbook.* Plume: New York. **395:** Pew Internet. www.pewinternet.org. **395:** Manago, A. M., T.

Taylor, and P. M. Greenfield. 2012. Me and my 400 friends: The anatomy of college students' Facebook networks, their communication patterns, and well-being. *Developmental Psychology* 48:369–380. **408:** Federal Trade Commission. http://www.ftc.gov/opa/2011/09/reebok.shtm. **409:** Federal Trade Commission. http://www.ftc.gov/bcp/edu/microsites/redflag. **415:** National Institutes of Health. http://health.nih.gov/topic/VitaminandMineralSupplements. **426:** Science, M., et al. 2012. Zinc or the treatment of the common cold: A systematic review and meta-analysis of randomized controlled trials. *Canadian Medical Association Journal* 184(10):E551–561.

Photo Credits

1: Rubberball/Getty Images. **2:** © BananaStock/PunchStock. **4:** (left) MichaelSvoboda/Getty Images, (right) © JLP/Jose L. Paleez/Corbis. **8:** (clockwise, from top left) © Royalty-Free/Jupiterimages, © Thinkstock Images/Jupiterimages, Stockbyte/Getty Images, © Royalty-Free/Corbis, © Tom & Dee Ann McCarthy/Corbis. **10:** (clockwise, from top left) © PhotoDisc/Getty Images, © Ryan McVay/Getty Images, © Brand X Pictures/Punchstock, Dorgie Productions/Getty Images, © Royalty-Free/Getty Images, © Karl Weatherly/Getty Images. **21:** Ingram Publishing. **23:** © LWA-Stephen Welstead/Corbis. **28:** Getty Images/Photodisc. **31:** (left) © BananaStock/PunchStock, (right) © Royalty-Free/PunchStock. **33:** © Jose Luis Pelaez, Inc./Corbis. **43:** Getty Images. **44:** © Digital Vision/PunchStock. **47:** Courtesy of Vibram USA. **49:** © Liquidlibrary/PictureQuest. **51:** © Dennis Welsh/PunchStock. **65:** Aurora Open/Whit Richardson/Getty Images. **78:** Blend Images/Getty Images. **85:** Eyewire/Getty Images. **91:** © Bob Winsett/Corbis. **92:** Signature Treadmill Desks. **101:** © Jim Cummins/Corbis. **104:** PureStock/Getty Images. **107:** The McGraw-Hill Companies, Inc./Christopher Kerrigan, photographer. **110:** Photo provided by NYCewheels.com. **111:** Image Source/Corbis. **117:** Comstock Images. **124:** Photodisc/Getty Images. **127:** (left) © Creatas Images/PunchStock, (right) © PhotoDisc/Getty Images. **139:** Ingram Publishing. **143:** © Thinkstock Images/JupiterImages.

145: Ryan McVay/Getty Images. **146:** Courtesy of Professional Disc Golf Association. **147:** JupiterImages/Creatas/Alamy. **159:** Royalty-Free/Corbis. **160:** © Corbis—All Rights Reserved. **164:** Image provided courtesy of Technogym, Inc. **166:** Mark Ahn Creative Services (with appreciation to Orangetheory Fitness®, Chandler, AZ). **166:** (bottom) Blend Images/Getty Images. **170:** © Royalty-Free/Corbis. **189:** © Charles B. Corbin. **199:** © Royalty-Free/Corbis. **204:** © Royalty-Free/Corbis. **206:** RubberBall/Alamy. **210:** © PhotoDisc/Getty Images. **212:** © Royalty-Free/JupiterImages. **225:** Ryan McVay/Getty Images. **231:** ©Thinkstock Images/Jupiterimages. **232:** ©Thinkstock Images/Jupiterimages. **236:** (top) Jonathon Ross/Cutcaster. **236:** (photo of woman standing, two photos of women lying down) Mark Ahn Creative Services (with appreciation to Orangetheory Fitness®, Chandler, AZ). **237:** (top left, 3 photos of woman lifting boxes) Ken Karp for MMH, (bottom right) © Creatas Images/Jupiter Images, (bottom left) © Stockdisc/PunchStock, (top right) Ingram Publishing/SuperStock. **265:** U.S. Air Force photo by Staff Sgt. Desiree N. Palacios. **267:** © David Pu'u/Corbis. **268:** Ingram Publishing. **271:** © Brand X Pictures/Superstock. **272:** © Corbis—All Rights Reserved. **274:** (all images) Rubberball/Getty Images. **289:** © Royalty-Free/Jupiter Images. **292:** ©JGI/Blend Images LLC. **302:** (left) © Jose Luis Pelaez Inc/Blend Images LLC, (right) © Peter Ciresa/Index Stock Imagery. **328:** © Image Shop/Corbis. **329:** Blend Images/Getty Images. **332:** © BananaStock/PunchStock. **340:** © PhotoDisc/Getty Images. **349:** Jack Hollingsworth/Blend Images LLC. **355:** Teo Lannie/GettyImages. **356:** © Photo courtesy of Body-Media, Inc. **358:** © Jose Luis Palaez, Inc. **367:** © McGraw-Hill Companies, Inc./Gary He, photographer. **369:** © James Russell/Corbis. **372:** © Corbis. **383:** © Royalty-Free/Corbis. **388:** © Fancy Photography/Veer. **394:** Design Pics/Don Hammond. **405:** © Imageshop/Punchstock. **407:** © Royalty-Free/Corbis. **409:** © Ariel Skelley/Getty Images. **411:** © Ingram Publishing/SuperStock. **413:** © Jose Luis Pelaez, Inc./Corbis. **414:** © Stockbyte. **423:** © Jeremy Woodhouse/Blend Images LLC. **426:** © Pixtal/SuperStock. **429:** © Getty Images/Purestock.

Index

FITNESS AND WELLNESS

Connect Fitness and Wellness is an integrated program that gives students access to a wealth of interactive online content, including fitness labs and self-assessments, video activities, quizzes, and other assignable activities based on the content in *Concepts of Physical Fitness*. All *Connect* content can be accessed directly from within any course management system with a single sign-on.

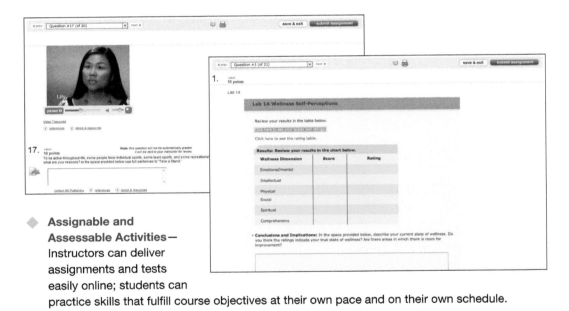

◆ **Assignable and Assessable Activities**—Instructors can deliver assignments and tests easily online; students can practice skills that fulfill course objectives at their own pace and on their own schedule.

◆ **Interactive Lab Activities**—Interactive lab activities provide students with instant feedback about their current level of fitness and wellness based on their personalized performance results. Students can then use this feedback to create their own individualized programs for behavior change.

◆ **Media-rich eBook**—The eBook contains embedded video clips, full-color images, links to discipline-specific sites, key terms and definitions, and behavior change tools.

◆ **Real-time Reports**—These printable, exportable reports show how well each student (or section) is performing on each course segment. Instructors can use this feature to spot problem areas before they crop up on an exam.